THE SMEATONIANS
The Society of Civil Engineers

John Smeaton by Thomas Gainsborough

THE SMEATONIANS
The Society of Civil Engineers

Garth Watson

CB, BSc(Eng) (London), HonDSc(City),
FICE, FIEE, HonMSCET, Chartered Engineer

Thomas Telford, London

Published by Thomas Telford Ltd,
Thomas Telford House, 1 Heron Quay, London E14 9XF

First published 1989

British Library Cataloguing in Publication Data
Watson, Garth
The Smeatonians: the Society of Civil Engineers
1. Great Britain. Civil Engineering, history
I. Title
624'.0941

ISBN: 0 7277 1526 7

Typeset in Great Britain by Pentacor Ltd, High Wycombe, Bucks
Printed and bound in Great Britain by Redwood Burn Limited,
Trowbridge, Wilts

Preface

In a Society which for more than 200 years has pursued its original purpose of bringing together those in the engineering profession "in a friendly way, to shake hands together and be personally known to each other", the history of the Smeatonians is largely about the lives of its members. The profession of a civil engineer was first identified in the middle of the 18th century, when some who had started their careers as skilled craftsmen became heavily engaged in public works and private undertakings of great magnitude. They recognised one another's achievements and in the early days of the Society distinguished themselves from those they called "artists or ingenious workmen and artificers."

Although it was not intended to be a learned society, the members took some interest in the works upon which their fellow members and others were engaged. Only after the reform of the Society in 1793 did it take on the additional purpose of promoting and communicating knowledge in the field of engineering. Neither did it set out to establish the qualifications of an engineer, beyond entitling some of its members to describe themselves as "Members of the Society of Civil Engineers of London".

It was the Institution of Civil Engineers, founded in 1818 and formed to establish a special centre of information and instruction for those following or intending to follow the profession of a civil engineer, which was the learned society and became in course of time, the qualifying body. At first it was necessary to be engaged in engineering works of great magnitude, practising on one's own account, to be recognised as a civil engineer, but by 1839 the Institution required candidates for its Roll to have been regularly educated "according to the usual routine of pupillage", and the original qualification was relegated to second place. The universities and colleges were slow to take up the new studies of engineering science, but when professional examinations were introduced by the Institution in 1897 those which provided courses in engineering were not slow to seek exemption for their graduates. University training, when it came, did not displace pupillage but provided an alternative, requiring a shorter period of practical training after an academic education.

These developments can be traced through the lives of the members of the Smeatonian Society. The 18th century engineers qualified for membership by their own achievements; in the 19th century it was by their master and pupil relationships; in the late Victorian era and in the 20th century, the academic route grew in prominence. The engineers who played a vital part in the industrial revolution and in the rising prosperity of Victorian times, were individuals of courage, imagination and skill, who showed great confidence in their own ability; many are household names.

When the 20th century began, partnerships were formed and limited companies floated. The great works upon which these engineers were engaged were the products of teamwork and their originators are for the most part anonymous. But they and their successors are the eminent engineers of today, many of whom are members of the Society.

The names of all the members are recorded in the annals of the Society and are listed here. The achievements of the early engineers are described and others only mentioned briefly; inevitably many whose membership added no less lustre to the Society have had to be left out.

Any history which pre-dates 1752 has difficulty in avoiding the confusion which can arise from the changes in the calendar. There were two changes; first, eleven days were removed so that a birth recorded before 2 September 1752 has anniversaries which appear to be eleven days later; secondly, the beginning of the year was changed from 26 March to 1 January. These adjustments affected the first 60 or so members of the Society, i.e. from Thomas Yeoman and John Smeaton to James Watt; for example, Smeaton's birth is correctly recorded as 28 May 1724 (old style) or 8 June 1724 (new style) the latter being relevant to anniversaries after 1752. Robert Mylne suffered both changes, his date of birth being 3 January 1733 (old style) or 14 January 1734 (new style).

The Minutes of meetings of the Society, complete from its foundation to the present day, are the main source of information about its activities. These and other records have been carefully preserved by successive Treasurers.

Thanks are due to Professor A.W. Skempton for his compilation of the list of members from 1771 to 1947, his "Duo-Centenary Notes" and the paper "Early Members of the Society" given by himself and

Dr Esther Wright to the Newcomen Society. Supplementary information has been taken from the obituaries in the *Proceedings* of the Institution of Civil Engineers and other institutions, the *Dictionary of National Biography* and *Who was Who*.

I acknowledge with gratitude the help of M.M. Chrimes, BA, MLS, ALA, Librarian, and Mrs Mary Murphy, ALA, Archivist, of the Institution of Civil Engineers.

The researcher reaps his own reward. I have discovered that Admiral Sir Richard Vesey Hamilton, who resigned from the Society on leaving London in January 1894, wrote from his new abode in Hampshire, the house where I now live. Major General O'Callaghan who was elected in 1912, shared the same staircase in our London flats, though his was two floors below mine. Such coincidences are the spice of life.

Garth Watson

Contents

Illustrations

Introduction

When John Smeaton described himself as a civil engineer for the first time, on the title page of his "Review of the Forth and Clyde Navigation" in 1768, he did more than differentiate his calling from that of the military engineer: he identified a new profession.

The development of public works is a vital part of the growth of civilisation. The industrial revolution, which called for more iron-works, coal mines and factories, brought in its train the movement of population from scattered rural communities to close knit industrial towns. This was made possible by the large scale production of food, achieved by the reclamation of land, irrigation and drainage, and the development of water supplies.

Industry required mechanical power greater than wind and water could provide, so industrial enterprises were located where best suited for access to raw materials, including coal, giving rise to a demand for internal navigation which was also needed between factory and factory and from warehouse to harbour. The sea-ports, sited as natural havens, had to be developed as commercial harbours for the transit of the raw materials and the manufactured goods of industry.

The drainage of the Fens was one of the most important projects of the 17th century; by 1653 over 300,000 acres of the Great Level had been reclaimed for food production. This was essential to meet the needs of the population in the growing industrial towns of the Midlands.

Land drainage and the improvement of river navigations served the needs of food production, water supply and bulk transport. The construction of turnpikes, arterial canals and the improvement of harbours followed; the railways came later. These projects called for expert designs and professional skills to bring them about. In Britain these skills were practised by the craftsmen who learned their trade by apprenticeship and passed on their knowledge and experience to the youngsters they in their turn brought up. There were millwrights, stonemasons and builders, surveyors, mechanics and instrument makers.

Experimental science developed in the 17th century. A group of scholars were meeting regularly in London by 1645, to study a new experimental philosophy. Some of them moved to Oxford during the Civil War and Protectorate; after the Restoration they went back to London to resume their meetings, at Gresham's College. They founded the Royal Society of London in 1660, which received its Royal Charter in 1662.

The craftsman's fund of knowledge, based on natural genius and practical experience, combined with the assimilation of scientific principles, generated a new profession. By the middle of the 18th century, at least a dozen men were well-known as engineers, acting as consultants in the design and construction of important engineering works and machinery, or in regular employment in charge of them. "They often met accidentally in the Houses of Parliament and in the Courts of Justice, each maintaining the propriety of his own designs without knowing much of each other", Robert Mylne stated.

It was suggested to Smeaton that such a state of the profession, then in its infancy, was improper. It would be good if meetings were to be held occasionally where they might come together in a social context: "Thus the sharp edges of their minds might be rubbed off, as it were, by a closer communication of ideas, no ways naturally hostile", said Mylne.

A number of them, including John Smeaton and Robert Mylne, in 1771 formed themselves into a society; they called it "The Society of Civil Engineers".

Chapter One

1771–1792

Seven of the leading engineers of the day met at the King's Head Tavern, Holborn, on 15 March 1771, and "agreed that the civil engineers of this Kingdom do form themselves into a Society consisting of a President, a Vice President, a Treasurer and Secretary and other Members". Meetings were to be held at the King's Head once a fortnight on Saturday evenings at seven o'clock, "from Christmas or so soon as any of the country members come to town (of which they shall give notice to the President) to the end of the sitting of Parliament". They agreed that each member in town would pay a forfeit of one shilling for being absent. This resolution was witnessed by the signatures of all those present. Thomas Yeoman took the chair and was elected President; he also acted as Treasurer and Secretary for the time being, keeping the Minutes in a book which he bought for the purpose a few days later.

The co-founders with Yeoman were John Smeaton, Robert Mylne, Joseph Nickalls, John Grundy, John Thompson and J. King. Yeoman, 63 years of age, was the eldest. His early career had been spent in Northampton, where in 1743 he had erected the world's first water-powered cotton mill. He remained in Northampton for about 15 years, surveying the enclosures and the turnpike roads and making agricultural machinery. As early as 1754 he was engaged in canal schemes and was joint engineer with Smeaton for the River Lea Navigation. His later works included the Coventry Canal and the Stroudwater Canal. With James Brindley and John Golborne he was consulted on the Forth and Clyde Navigation, as the title page of Smeaton's 1768 review shows.

Smeaton, although 16 years Yeoman's junior, was one of the most influential members of the Society and he attended the meetings regularly throughout his life. His leading role, although never as President, was recognised in the re-naming of the Society after his death. He was born on 8 June 1724 (new style), at Austhorpe Lodge near Leeds, where his father was a practising lawyer. For six years from the age of ten, he attended Leeds Grammar School. In 1742 he was sent to London to study law, but his interest was in mechanical things and astronomy, both of which he pursued in his workshop at home. In London he met members of the Royal Society and, no doubt influenced by them, forsook the law and became a scientific instrument maker. By 1748 he was well established in London and by 1753 he had turned to engineering as the source of his livelihood. Two years later he made a five week tour of the Low Countries to study engineering works there.

His early works were concerned with the design and construction of windmills and watermills. But when the proprietors of the Eddystone Lighthouse sought the advice of the President of the Royal Society, Lord Macclesfield, after the old lighthouse had been destroyed, he recommended Smeaton to them. For the next four years, Smeaton was engaged on the design and construction of the new lighthouse. Not to the exclusion of other work, however; he was concerned with the Calder and Hebble Navigation, Coldstream and Perth bridges, Potteric Carr and Adlingfleet drainage schemes, St Ives and Eyemouth harbours, and he worked with Yeoman on the River Lea. In Scotland he reported on the Forth and Clyde Canal, on improvements in the River Clyde and on Dysart harbour.

At the same time he was pursuing experiments in water power and the power of the wind, which led to his important paper, "An Experimental Enquiry concerning the Natural Powers of Water and Wind to turn Mills and other Machines depending on a Circular Motion", which he read before the Royal Society, of which he had been made a Fellow in 1753. He was given its highest award, the Copley Medal.

To his professional engineering services was added the Receivership of the Greenwich Hospital's Derwentwater estates in Durham and Northumberland, to which he was appointed in 1764. It provided a modest but steady income. By 1771 Smeaton was pre-eminent among the steadily increasing number of engineers.

Robert Mylne, nine years younger than Smeaton, came of a long line of architects and masons. He was born at Edinburgh, where his father, Thomas, as well as being the City Surveyor, had his own extensive architectural practice. Robert left Edinburgh in April 1754 and studied architecture in Rome for the next four years. After travelling through Switzerland and Holland, he reached London in 1759, in time to enter the competition for the design and construction of Blackfriars Bridge. His design, although controversial at the time, was preferred to those of Smeaton, Phillips and others, and it was approved in 1760. The bridge was completed in 1769.

A

R E V I E W

O F

S E V E R A L   M A T T E R S

R E L A T I V E   T O

THE FORTH AND CLYDE NAVIGATION,
as now fettled by ACT of PARLIAMENT :

W I T H

SOME OBSERVATIONS on the REPORTS

O F

Meff. BRINDLEY, YEOMAN, and GOLBURNE.

By JOHN SMEATON, CIVIL ENGINEER, and F. R. S.

[*Publifhed by order of a General Meeting of the Company of Proprietors
of the* FORTH *and* CLYDE *Navigation* (1ft *November* 1768.)
for the ufe of the Proprietors.]

Printed by R. FLEMING and A. NEILL.
M,DCC,LXVIII.

Title page of Review of Forth and Clyde Navigation

Mylne's works encompassed many bridges and country houses, and also public buildings. In London the most notable were the City of London Lying-in Hospital and Offices for the New River Company at Clerkenwell, built soon after his appointment as engineer to the Company in 1770. This appointment did not interfere with his continuing private engineering practice.

Joseph Nickalls was a year younger than Smeaton. He had trained as a millwright, and from 1759 to 1761 he was Smeaton's resident engineer on the Calder and Hebble Navigation. As Smeaton's assistant he worked on the London Bridge water wheel project in 1767–68. He surveyed the Thames between Maidenhead and Reading for the Thames Commissioners, and not only drew up plans for improving the Thames Navigation but successfully presented the case for it in the Parliamentary Committee in 1771, against opposition from the promoters of canal schemes.

Grundy—"John Grundy of Spalding, Engineer," as he described himself—had an extensive practice in the Eastern counties. He was born in 1719; his father, also called John, was a land surveyor and a renowned mathematician. Under his father's direction John carried out the repairs after breaches of the sea walls on the Norfolk coast in 1742. He was later employed by the Earl of Lincoln to report on the drainage of the Borough Fen. His main work was in the improvement of river navigations and the drainage of adjacent low lands. He reported on the River Witham from Boston to Lincoln in 1743, but no action was taken then and he revised his recommendations ten years later; Langley Edwards made alternative proposals in 1760, and then Smeaton was called in; the three met and made a joint report the following year. The Bill went before Parliament in 1762. When Grundy made proposals to drain the low ground east of the River Hull in Holderness, Smeaton was commissioned to give a second opinion. In 1770 Grundy was involved in improvements to the River Nene outfall below Wisbech. His later works included the first dock at Hull.

Although a John Thompson and a J. King were present at the inaugural meeting of the Society on 15 March and both signed the Minute Book, neither continued in active membership. Thompson came from Spalding and was probably one of John Grundy's group of drainage engineers. King's address was given as Essex, but no more is known about him. Their names were included in the first list of members drawn up in 1782 but when the revised list was compiled in 1784 their names were among those scored out for non-attendance.

At the second meeting of the Society, on 29 March, Thomas Yeoman, the President was in the chair; Robert Mylne was elected

Vice President, and the meeting days were changed from fortnightly on Saturdays to weekly on Fridays. The forfeit money from absentees was to be used for the general expenditure incurred in running the Society and in addition a subscription of 3*d* a week was imposed with effect from 15 March.

At this meeting three new members joined, John Golborne, Robert Whitworth and William Black; all three signed the Minute Book. Golborne lived at Chester; he was for many years the engineer of the River Dee Company and was the engineer for the improvements in the River Weaver Navigation. In 1768 he was recommended to the Forth and Clyde Canal proprietors by Brindley, and his work deepening the Clyde below the city of Glasgow was completed in 1775. Golborne and Yeoman both reported on the drainage of the North Level in the Fens and on the River Nene outfall in 1769. Grundy's report was made in 1770 and the work was carried out with Golborne in charge. Golborne was active in the Fens again in 1777, when his report was based on surveys made by Robert Whitworth.

Whitworth, who was born in 1734, was Brindley's principal assistant from 1767 until Brindley's death in 1772. He worked on plans for the Coventry Canal, the Birmingham Canal and the Oxford Canal; he surveyed the line of the Leeds and Liverpool Canal in 1768; his plans, profiles and soundings of the Thames from Maidenhead to Mortlake were fine examples of his survey work, and he produced the maps of Brindley's Canals which were published in 1769. He also worked in Ireland. After Brindley's death, Whitworth developed his own extensive engineering practice, mainly in canals, until in 1785 he was appointed Chief Engineer of the Forth and Clyde Canal and later of the Leeds and Liverpool Canal. In 1795 he took over the Herefordshire and Gloucestershire Canal.

William Black was not an engineer; he was a Trustee of the Holderness (East Yorks) Drainage scheme, about which Smeaton had been consulted in 1763, and which was designed and carried out by Grundy. It was completed in 1768. Black attended the meetings of the Society from time to time until May 1774, but his name was deleted when the 1784 list of members was compiled.

The only other member elected in 1771, the year of the Society's foundation, was Hugh Henshall. Brindley had married Henshall's young sister, Anne, in 1765 and thereafter Henshall was closely associated with Brindley's work. Brindley himself did not join the Society; by 1771 he was a sick man, suffering from diabetes, and he died the following year.

Henshall's father, John, was a land surveyor and he trained his son in surveying. Hugh was engaged on the surveys of the Staffordshire

LIST OF THE MEM·BERS

OF THE

SOCIETY OF CIVIL ENGINEERS.

ORIGINAL MEMBERS, 1771.

THOMAS YEOMAN, *President.*
ROBERT MYLNE, *Vice-President.*
JOHN SMEATON.
JOSEPH NICKALLS.
JOHN GRUNDY.
JOHN THOMPSON.
J. KING.
JOHN GOLBORNE.
W. BLACK.
ROBERT WHITWORTH.
HUGH HENSHALL.

MEMBERS ELECTED FROM 1772 TO 1792.

Date of Election.		Date of Election.	
1772	JOHN SMITH.	1777	JOHN PINKERTON.
„	WILLIAM IVESON.	„	Mr. PIERCE.
„	JOHN HOLMES.	1778	Mr. NAIRN.
„	WILLIAM MATHEWS.	„	Mr. WALFORD.
„	Mr. HOGARTH.	1780	JAMES COWPER.
1773	WILLIAM JESSOP.	„	MATTHEW BOULTON.
„	LANGLEY EDWARDS.	„	JOHN WHITEHURST.
„	JOSEPH PRIESTLY.	„	GRAHAM WILKINSON.
„	JOHN LONGBOTTOM.	„	LUKE HOGARD.
„	JOHN GOTT.	1781	REUBEN BURROW.
1774	JOSEPH PAGE.	„	THOMAS MARTIN.
„	MAJOR HENRY WATSON.	„	WILLIAM THOMAS.
„	Mr. McHALE.	„	JAMES ARROW.
„	CHRISTOPHER PINCHBECK.	„	SAMUEL WYATT.
„	WILLIAM DE BRAHM.	1782	STEPHEN PENNY NICKSON.
„	JOHN MONK.	„	Mr. NORTHCOATE.
„	WILLIAM THOMPSON.	1783	Mr. SNAPE.
1776	WILLIAM MURDOCH.	„	Mr. BUTLER.
„	Mr. MACKENZIE.	„	Mr. DADFORD.
„	EDWARD GASCOIGNE.	1785	JOHN RENNIE.
„	JOHN COWPER.	1786	GEORGE YOUNG.
„	Mr. HANUM.	1789	HENRY EASTBURNE.
„	WILLIAM FADEN.	„	JAMES WATT.
„	SAMUEL PHILLIPS.	„	Mr. MARGUAND.
„	Mr. FRUIN.	„	Mr. JACOB.
1777	JOHN JARDIN.	1791	Rev. HENRY GREEN.
„	THOMAS MORRIS.	1792	Mr. CRAIG.
„	REUBEN HODGKINSON.	„	JOSEPH HODSKINSON.

List of members, 1771–92

and Worcestershire Canal and drew up plans for the Trent and Mersey Canal, becoming the resident engineer under Brindley for the first six years of its construction, 1766–72. After Brindley died, Henshall succeeded him as Chief Engineer of the Trent and Mersey Canal and he was the engineer of the Chesterfield Canal.

When the second session of the Society started on 27 March 1772, two new members were admitted, John Smith and William Iveson. Smith, who had worked on the western division of the River Nene Navigation when Yeoman was the engineer, had been trained by his father, the engineer of the River Don Navigation, and both father and son were engaged on the Yorkshire Ouse. John Smith, jnr, later carried out works on the Ouse above York about which he sought the advice of Smeaton. He had given evidence, with Smeaton and Grundy, before the House of Commons Committee considering the Ouse Navigation Bill in 1767.

William Iveson was a solicitor, and although he signed the Minute Book on being elected, he never attended again.

Two more members were nominated at that same meeting and were elected the following week; they were John Holmes and William Mathews, both clockmakers. Holmes was a kinsman of Smeaton, his lifelong friend and biographer. He had a high reputation as a clockmaker and built the turret clock for Greenwich Hospital. He acted as agent for Smeaton in London, not only in his engineering practice but also in his business for the Derwentwater estates of Greenwich Hospital. Mathews was equally highly regarded, and was one of three assessors appointed to examine John Harrison's chronometer in 1764. Thomas Hogarth was another drainage engineer and was elected in May, but he never attended the meetings.

At the meeting on 27 March 1772, all forfeits and weekly subscriptions were abolished and an entrance fee of 1s imposed. This was a surprising decision, as each new member paid an entrance fee only once, whereas the general expenditure was a continuing commitment, mainly for printed notices and their delivery. As it turned out however, the steady increase in new members provided sufficient income to meet the current needs of the Society for several years.

In May a box was bought, with a lock and two keys, one to be held by the President, and the other by the Vice President. The box was needed to house the Minute Book and the archives of the Society and it became the repository for cash when there was any. For the most part the Society was in debt to the President (in his capacity as Treasurer), who kept an account in the back of the Minute Book and advanced money whenever the Society needed it.

In March 1773 there were five admissions: William Jessop, Smeaton's protégé, pupil and assistant; Langley Edwards of King's Lynn, the Fen drainage engineer who, sadly, died the following year; Joseph Priestly of Bradford; John Longbottom, engineer of the Leeds and Liverpool Canal; and John Gott, a bridge engineer, surveyor of the West Riding of Yorkshire, who had been the resident engineer under Jessop on the Aire and Calder Navigation. At this meeting the frequency of future meetings was changed from weekly to once a fortnight, but in the 1774 session weekly meetings were resumed.

On 22 April 1774 William Jessop was appointed Secretary, "so long as he shall be in town during the sessions of Parliament". He had set up his own practice as a consulting engineer in 1772 and joined the Society the following year. He attended regularly until March 1777 when he became a country member, but in March 1792 he resumed his regular attendance, giving his address as Southampton Street, Strand.

Joseph Page, and Robert McHale the engineer of the Forth and Clyde Canal, were elected early in 1774 but did not become active members. At the meeting on 29 April three new members were enrolled: Major Henry Watson, Christopher Pinchbeck and William De Brahm. Although the title "civil engineer" had been adopted to differentiate the profession from that of the military engineer, the Society soon admitted to membership distinguished Army and Navy engineers (and in modern times Air Force engineers too).

Watson was the first military man to be elected. He was born at Holbeach, Lincs., in 1737 and entered the Royal Military Academy, Woolwich, in 1755, where he developed a talent for mathematics. He saw active service in the Army until, in 1763, he was recommended by Clive to go to India. In the rank of captain he was Field Engineer and Commander of the troops in Bengal in 1764, and was sworn into the service of the East India Company. His next appointment was Chief Engineer of Bengal, Bihar and Orissa. He planned and started the construction of the docks and fitting-out yard in Calcutta. He also designed and built two sloops, *Nonsuch*, 36 guns and *Surprise*, 32 guns, which were later used in commerce. Watson joined the Society after returning to England early in 1774; he was promoted to Lieutenant Colonel the following year. He was recalled to India in 1780 and was joined there by Reuben Burrow, the mathematician and former assistant to Dr Maskelyne at the Royal Observatory. In January 1786 Watson resigned from the army on grounds of ill health and he died on the day he landed at Dover, 17 September.

Christopher Pinchbeck was a mathematical instrument maker who had several inventions to his credit and had been awarded a prize by the Society of Arts. At the meeting following his election he found himself in the chair, despite the presence of many members of long standing. It was the custom, when the President and Vice President were both absent, for the chair to be taken by the last member to enter the room before dinner was served, and Pinchbeck seemed frequently to qualify. He was one of the oldest members, only two years younger than Yeoman, whom he followed as President in 1781. William Thompson and John Monk were elected in May but Monk died in the following February.

The Society fulfilled a very important function. Engineers were frequently called upon by the promoters or proprietors of schemes to examine and report upon each others' work—not altogether surprising, at a time when the profession of engineering was developing and those who promoted and financed projects were unfamiliar with the matters put before them. Whenever a second opinion differed from the scheme proposed, it was fertile ground for the conflict of ideas to lead to personal acrimony. When Bills were before Parliament and its committees were examining them, the promoters on the one hand and the objectors on the other, would bring in well known engineers to give expert witness in support of their arguments. The River Navigation Authorities opposed the projects of the Canal Companies and both opposed the Turnpike Trusts. Controversy in the committee room could easily lead to personal conflict when professional reputations were at stake.

The founders of the Society saw the need for a meeting place where engineers could rub shoulders in a friendly atmosphere and get to know each other better. Thus the Society was formed and Mylne described how "conversation, argument and a social communication of ideas and knowledge in the particular walks of each member were, at the same time, the amusement and business of the meetings." This was not a learned Society but a dining club, which brought together those often in dispute. Technical matters were by no means excluded, however; in May 1774, the Secretary, Jessop, wrote to Gordon Brewer of Bow, asking for a demonstration of his newly invented piling machine, to be given to the members of the Society.

Murdoch McKenzie, the Hydrographer and Surveyor to the Admiralty, and Robert Hanum were elected in March 1776, but neither attended the meetings; Thomas Fruin, a drainage engineer working on the River Ancholme, Lincs., was elected in April.

Not all admitted to membership were engineers engaged upon works of importance; Edward Gascoigne, a locksmith, and John Cowper, a millwright, were also elected in March; and William Faden, a geographer, and Samuel Phillips, engine maker, in April.

After his election William De Brahm never attended. His name was included in the members list in 1782 but was omitted in 1784. Of those who never attended meetings, some had a legitimate excuse, for example, Thomas Hogarth was one of the group of engineers in Spalding who were concerned with the drainage of the Fens, and Robert McHale was engaged on the Clyde. But the non-participation of others like William De Brahm and Robert Hanum is less easily explained.

Notices of meetings were sent regularly to the members in London and attendance fluctuated widely from seven or eight in the early years to a dozen or so later. Sometimes, however, only two or three were present, so a quorum of five was fixed for the conduct of business. A gavel was bought in 1777, "to regulate the genius and control the spirit of the members". It cost 1s; and 9s 6d was paid for another box with a lock and two keys, and 1s charged for porterage to carry these purchases to the King's Head.

William Faden, the geographer, was a partner and the successor of Thomas Jeffreys, geographer to George III. In March 1777 Faden produced a copperplate of a "Summons Card", and 50 impressions of it, asking that they be accepted by the Society, "as a testimony of his esteem and regard for its honour and prosperity". The same summons, with only minor alterations, has been used ever since. At the meeting a vote of thanks was passed to Faden and also a resolution to increase the admission fee from 1s to 5s. The meeting closed with the election to membership of John Jardin, Thomas Morris, engineer of the Chester Canal, Reuben Hodgkinson and John Pinkerton, one of the earliest of public works contractors. The following week Pierce, the landlord of the King's Head, was elected a member, but instead of paying the customary fee, he gave those assembled a 3s bowl of punch.

In 1777, 28 March fell on Good Friday and the Minutes record that, "it being a fast day there was fish only for supper". That meetings were convivial can hardly be disputed, judging by the tone of the Minutes of successive meetings:

> "After passing a friendly meeting eating tripe, drinking a quantum sufficit, ye Society adjourned. . . . " "The evening was spent in missalanious [sic] conversation and profitable. Adjourned to this day se'en night, . . . " "This evening, after being spent Canalically, Hydraulically, Mathematically, Philosophically, Mechanically, Naturally and Sociably, was adjourned till Fryday next."

At the meeting in March 1778, Edward Nairne, the optical, mathematical and scientific instrument maker and electrician, and

Thomas Walford, described as a manufacturer, were admitted. Christopher Pinchbeck was elected Vice President; during the four years since he joined he had attended meetings regularly and had frequently taken the chair in accordance with custom. He continued his good record, taking the chair whenever the President was absent. On 28 April 1780 the President was too ill to attend and he was absent for the remainder of the session; he never attended again. Yeoman died on 24 January 1781 and Pinchbeck was elected President on 15 May. Hodgkinson was made the Vice President at the same meeting. A fortnight later Smeaton informed the members present that he was obliged to leave town in a few days time. It was resolved to adjourn until the next session.

James Cowper had joined his brother John as a member in April 1780. They were the leading millwrights in London, specialising in industrial machinery, especially the mechanical equipment of breweries. In May, Matthew Boulton was elected. His factory at Soho, Birmingham, was very successful in the production of metalware of all kinds; in 1772 he had entered into partnership with James Watt to form the firm of engine makers, Boulton and Watt. There were three more elections, John Whitehurst, scientist, Graham Wilkinson and Luke Hogard, two of Grundy's engineers based at Spalding.

Reuben Burrow, the mathematician and astronomer was elected in May 1781, but departed shortly afterwards to join Lieut. Col. Watson in India. Also in May, Thomas Martin and James Arrow, builder, were admitted, and two architects, William Thomas and Samuel Wyatt. Wyatt was the architect of Albion Mill, Blackfriars, the Commissioner's House, Portsmouth Dockyard, and Trinity House, London. There were two new members in 1782, Stephen Nickson, who resigned the following year, and James Northcoate, RA, the portrait and historical painter, a former student and assistant to Sir Joshua Reynolds.

In the absence of the President, Smeaton was in the chair for the opening meeting of the 1782 session, and he attended the next two meetings. On 3 May he presented to the Society a copy of his paper, published in 1760, on "The Natural Powers of Water and Wind", and Walford gave the Society a copy of "England's Improvements by Sea and Land", by Andrew Yarraton. Both gifts were gratefully acknowledged and recorded in the Minutes. It was agreed that those publications could be borrowed by any member upon his giving a receipt and an undertaking to return it in a fortnight.

At the end of the session a comprehensive list of members was prepared from the elections recorded in the Minutes and their addresses were added.

List of the Society of Civil Engineers
April 28 – 1786; In its Reformed State. —

Names	
1. John Smeaton Esqr	No. 2 – Grays Inn Court, Holborn.
2. Rob: Mylne Esqr	New River Head, Islington
3. Mr. Nichols Drinkwater —	Grand Lane, Southwark
4. Mr. Thomas Holmes	Near the ... to Church, Strand
5. Mr. John Cooper —	Pottpool Lane
6. Mr. Eden —	Dr. Hattons Lane
7. Mr. Phillips —	Black Fryars Road ...

† Mr. Jessop —	Prince Street, Spitalfields.
Mr. Hogg... Vice President	Arundel Street, Strand —
Mr. Nevie —	Cornhill, Royal Exchange
Mr. ... —	
Mr. Whitworth —	... Arms Inn, London Hall Street
Mr. William Jessop –	Southampton Street
Mr. Pinkerton —	
Mr. ... — — —	West Bromwich by Birmingham
Mr. Boulton Esqr	Albion Mills Black Fryars Road

List of members, 28 April 1786

Members Continued
Mr. Esthersom
Mr Kraft —   At Mr Matthews.
   No 6 — Green Lettice Lane Cannon Street.

Mr. Marquand   House Henry Road Westminster

Marshall — Wild wichstrut White Horse Fetter Lane

St. Michaells Alleigate

Charlotte Street Portland Place No 13.

Mr. Jacob proposed — No 56 South St Soho

When the next session started on 11 March 1783 the President was again absent, and Smeaton took the chair. At the meeting a fortnight later it was announced that Pinchbeck had died on 17 March. Nickalls was proposed as his successor, and elected unanimously. He had worked for Smeaton on many projects and had built his early reputation on the improvement of river navigations and the construction of canals. Since the founding of the Society he had been engaged in harbour improvements, at Dover in 1771, at Wells, Norfolk, in 1782, and he reported on Yarmouth Haven in 1783.

The outgoings of the Society were small, mainly for postage; seven letters cost 7d. The entrance fees proved adequate, leaving a small margin, usually a shilling or two, in the box. When there was a deficit, the Treasurer, advanced the required sum and recouped it later. In April 1783 there was 17s 6d in the box and 4s 6d was withdrawn on 13 May. It was proposed at the meeting on 27 May that the cash in the box go towards payment of the dinner bill. This being the last meeting of the session, the matter was held over. From the beginning of the following session a new practice was adopted which still prevails: each member attending paid a sum fixed from time to time by general agreement, and any shortfall or surplus after the tavern bill had been paid, was borne by the general fund of the Society. Thereafter the sum left in the box after "the reckoning" was paid, was recorded in the Minutes.

John Snape, a land surveyor from Moxhull, Warwicks., who was working on the Birmingham Canal, joined in March 1783: Dr Butler, DD, of Gray's Inn, who joined at the same meeting, was introduced by Smeaton who had moved into chambers there. Thomas Dadford Brindley's assistant, who worked on the Dudley Canal and the Trent and Mersey Canal and became a contractor undertaking construction of the Cromford Canal in 1789 and the Glamorgan Canal in 1790, also joined. In June 1784 a comprehensive list of members' names and addresses was compiled. The names of those who had died and all those who had not attended during the previous 12 months were crossed out. There were 42 names on the original list but 23 were deleted. The 17 members normally in London, who were to be summoned to meetings, were marked with a cross.

The 1785 session started with the President, Joseph Nickalls in the chair; Hodgkinson the Vice President and Smeaton were among those present and John Rennie was elected a member. The President chaired the meeting a week later, missed two, but attended again on 6 May and then was absent for the remainder of the session. At the last meeting, on 8 July, a hint of reproach was evident when it was recorded that the meeting "adjourned 'till the President is pleased to call the next meeting, to whom this meeting leaves the consideration of the President's absence, it having been called at his special request".

The next session opened on 18 November 1785, but adjourned after three meetings, "'till the President thinks proper to issue his summons."

Meetings did not resume until 31 March 1786, when George Young, surveyor, was elected. The list of members was revised again, deleting those known to have died and eliminating those who had not attended meetings for 12 months: 22 names remained on the list, which was approved at the meeting on 28 April, when Smeaton was in the chair and Mylne, Jessop and Rennie were among those present. It was reviewed in July 1787 when those whose names remained on the list amounted to 20 members and there was one candidate. A proposal that meetings be held once a month in future was deferred, this being the last meeting of the 1787 session; it was not brought up again.

The minutes record that the Society continued to meet and adjourn during the remainder of the year 1787, and during the whole of 1788 without any alteration or new regulation during that time. At the meeting on 23 January 1789 only two members were present, Mylne and Martin. The Minutes state, "The President who ordered this meeting did not attend nor send any excuse". A meeting was summoned for the following week, which Nickalls the President did attend, and Mylne, Jardin and Rennie were there. Mylne moved that they meet next on 13 February, "in conformity to the original principles of the Society and that summonses be issued once a fortnight 'till further orders".

At the March meeting Henry Eastburn, who had succeeded William Jessop as Smeaton's assistant at Austhorpe Lodge, was elected. He was Smeaton's nephew and, like Jessop, had been his pupil. At the next meeting James Watt was proposed and duly elected. Watt was born at Greenock in 1736 and at the age of 18 went to London to work as a mathematical instrument maker. Ill health compelled him to return to Glasgow, where he worked in the University. He set himself up as a surveyor working on engineering schemes. In 1764, while repairing a model Newcomen engine, he turned his attention to the efficiency of steam engines and in 1765 invented the separate condenser. He went into partnership with John Roebuck of the Carron Ironworks in 1768, and took out his patent in 1769. By 1772 Matthew Boulton was Watt's partner, and their main work was the design, manufacture and installation of pumping engines in mines. In 1781 Watt developed the rotatory motion engine, and the following year patented the double-acting steam engine. He joined the Society in 1789, but being based and resident in Birmingham his attendance was relatively infrequent. John Marquand and Joseph Jacob also joined in 1789. James Playfair, architect, and the Reverend Henry Green were elected in 1791.

An alteration to the summons card was approved in April 1789, and Faden was asked to modify the copperplate by adding the words "of Civil Engineers" after the word "Society".

A revised list of members was approved on 29 May. It contained only the names of the 20 who had attended within the previous 12 months; of those, summonses were to be sent regularly to 12. In the 1790 session, meetings were held fortnightly from April to June. The 1791 session ran from 17 December 1790 to the following May. These followed the rule that meetings be held during the sessions of Parliament.

The Society was living on a shoestring. At the meeting on Tuesday, 6 December 1791, the tavern bill was £1 10s 5d, a tip of 2s 7d was added and the 11 members present paid 3s each. On Friday, 16 December, the bill was £1 6s 10d which with 2s 2d added amounted to £1 9s 0d, but eight members paid 3s 6d each, leaving Mylne the Treasurer to find 1s. No provision was made for the general expenses of the Society, e.g. the provision and delivery of summonses etc. It was then decided to impose a fine of 6d on each member who received a summons but who absented himself. Although the fines brought in 19s during January and February, Mylne had to advance another shilling before the month was out. It was 16 March before he got his money back, which left only 2s in the box.

At this meeting Smeaton presented a book entitled *"An Account Of Some Experiments Upon Machinery For Measuring The Way Of A Ship At Sea"*. This gift was acknowledged in the Minutes and a vote of thanks passed. It was added to the list of those which the members were encouraged to borrow.

The opening meeting of the 1792 session was held on Friday, 11 November 1791, and the next meeting was on Tuesday, 6 December.

How the President, Joseph Nickalls, offended Smeaton was not recorded. That he did so is certain, and it is evident that many members took Smeaton's part. The Minutes for 6 December contain Nickall's abject apology:

"Mr Nickalls, on a representation of the offence given Mr Smeaton, expressed himself in the following terms; that he was mistaken, that he was sorry for the offence given Mr Smeaton and that he begged his pardon as a Member of the Society. It was

The True List, for Summoned

— Grays Inn —
1. New River Head, Islington
2. Gravel Lane, Christ Church, Surry
3. Port Pool Lane — Grays Inn Lane
4. Surry Road, Christ Church
5. Ferry Road, Christ Church
6. a Country Member —
7. Arundel Street – Strand
   a Country Member
8. Strand, — Opposite New Church
9. Strand — Corner of St Martins Lane
   a Country Member
10. St Michaels Corn hill
    a Country Member
#. Horse ferry Road – Westminster —
11. No. 7, Throgmorton ... Place
12. No. 13, Charlotte Street ...
13. No. ... New Road
##. Great Scotland Yard

A Revised List of this Society was made ...
... those who have altered @ within
the twelve month, ... is follows —

- John Smeaton, Esqr "F.R.S. Civil Engineer —
- Robert Mylne, Esqr. F.R.S. Civil Engineer
- Mr Joseph Nickalls — President. — Civil Engineer
- Mr Cooper — Civil Engineer
- Mr Phillips — Civil Engineer
- Mr Pereve — Civil Engineer
- Mr Jessop — Civil Engineer
- Mr Hodkinson — Civil Engineer
- Mr Whitworth — Civil Engineer
- Mr Holmes
- Mr Forden
- Mr Nape
- Mr Martin
- Mr Eastburne
- Mr Marquand
- Mr Jevie
- Mr Wilkinson
- Our Thomas as
- Mr Craig

List of members, 16 December 1791

thereupon moved that the said apology should be entered upon the Minutes of this meeting".

Before this latter motion was put, the "previous question" was moved; had it been passed, the apology would have gone unrecorded, but it was negatived. So the main question "for the entry in the Minutes" was put and carried in the affirmative. There were ten members present including Smeaton and Nickalls.

Ending on a happier note, the Minutes recorded the birth of a child to John Rennie; it was his firstborn, a son, who was named George.

A new list of members was compiled, again containing only the names of those who had attended within the past 12 months. Of the 18 members listed, ten were designated "Civil Engineer" and four were country members.

Although the Society continued to be dominated by the most eminent engineers of the day, a significant number of the members were not designated civil engineers nor entitled to be. This led to some discontent, which surfaced in 1792. At a well attended meeting on 30 March it was agreed that, in the future admission of members, only those who were practising in the profession of civil engineering would be members, the others would be called "honorary" members. Charles Alexander Craig, a surveyor at the Office of Works, was the first to be elected an honorary member under the new rule. At the next meeting Joseph Hodskinson, surveyor, was also elected an honorary member.

The new rule could not disguise the fact that after 20 years of the Society's existence, comparatively few of its members were employed in public works or private undertakings of real magnitude. The other members were described by Mylne as "workmen and artificers connected with and employed in, works of engineering". Reform of the Society, in accordance with its original purpose, was discussed among the principal members, and decided upon in May 1792. A committee of reorganisation was appointed, comprising Mylne, Whitworth, Jessop and Rennie. Smeaton agreed to be a member, but before its first meeting could be held he had died.

The 1792 session ended in May, and Smeaton, who had attended all but two of the 13 meetings of the session between 6 December and 25 May, returned to Austhorpe Lodge in June. While walking in the garden in mid September he suffered a stroke, from the effects of which he died on 28 October. He was buried in the Parish Church at Whitkirk where there is a mural monument to his memory.

Chapter Two

1793–1811

The committee of reorganisation met for the first time on 15 April 1793, at the York Tavern and Coffee House, Blackfriars. The aim was to renew the Society "in a better and more respectable form", according to Mylne. At this first meeting it was agreed that there should be three classes of membership.

Those who were actually engaged in design and construction of engineering works of all kinds would be considered "First Class" members. As honorary members there would be various "Artists" whose professions and employments were a necessary and useful part of engineering; and a class of "Gentlemen" would also be designated honorary members. Resolutions were drafted to regulate the conduct of business and to define the procedures for the nomination and election of members. At the next meeting of the committee, on 27 April, the draft resolutions were read, amended and approved.

As a temporary measure it was agreed to meet weekly during the 1793 session, in order to complete and modify if necessary the rules and regulations of the reformed Society. A letter was sent to those selected for membership, asking if they would accept nomination. Those accepting would be put to a ballot of the members.

In the class of engineers, designated "Members of the First Class", the names of the four committee members were the first to be recorded; Mylne, founder member, Vice President until superseded by Pinchbeck in 1778, and Treasurer of the reformed Society; Whitworth, a member since 1771; Jessop, elected in 1773; and Rennie, who had joined in 1785. An invitation to rejoin was accepted by James Watt, a member from 1789, and three newcomers were invited and duly elected. They were James Golborne, the nephew and former pupil of John Golborne who had died in 1783, Sir Thomas Hyde Page, a military engineer, and John Duncombe, Jessop's assistant on the Ellesmere Canal.

The class of "Artists", was specifically defined. There was to be a geographer, a time-keeper maker, two instrument makers, two land

1st It was Agreed that no Gentlemen should become a Member of this Society, except those who are actually employed in Designing, & forming, Works of different kinds, in the Various Departments of Engineering.

2nd That there shall be a class of Gentlemen in addition thereto, and forming a part of the said Society under the denomination of honorary Members.

3rd That in the said Class of honorary Members, there shall be admitted, various Artists, whose professions and employments, are necessary & useful thereto as well as connected with Civil Engineering.

4th That five Members shall form a Quorum for business.

5th That all Members shall be elected by Ballot; and that two thirds of the then voting Members, are necessary to be in favour of, & to elect a Member.

6th That all candidates for admission, shall be proposed, and seconded by two Members, at one Meeting and Ballotted for at the next or a following meeting.

7 That a Civil Engineer, shall preside as Chairman of the meeting for the time being; and the youngest member present shall Act as Secretary.

8 That a contribution of half a Guinea Annually, be collected of all the Members of the Society, to defray the fixed and general expenses as well as that of Summons.

9 That it will be expected, of every Member of the Society, whose Reports, Memoires, or Plans upon any Subject of Engineering, are printed published or given away, that a Copy thereof shall be deposited by them, as the property of the Society.

10 That it will be considered by the Society, as an obligation, of any Gentleman will present them with any papers, Plans or books on the Subject of Engineering, which heretofore have been published, on Subjects they were concerned in; or which they have been or shall be published by any person, not a member of this Society.

11 That the Secretary be injoined and required to enter all Articles of the Description above-mentioned in the Schedule or list of things belonging to the Society.

12 That the Rules and regulations, which form the Constitution of this Society, shall be printed, for the use of the Members, when they shall be finally settled.

13 That all Members of the first Class of this Society, shall, on proper occasions, assume the Style and Title of Member of the Society of Civil Engineers in London.

14 That the Meetings of this Society shall be during the Sessions of Parliament; and

15 That the same shall be held, once a fortnight, on the 1st and 3rd Saturday, of every month.

Rules and regulations, 1793

surveyors practising levelling, two millwrights, a printer and an engine maker; they were designated "Members of the Second Class". Three former members were admitted; William Faden, geographer, Samuel Phillips, engine maker, and George Young who re-entered as one of the land surveyors, the other being a new member, Thomas Milne. The rest were new to the Society; Jesse Ramsden and John Troughton filled the two vacancies for instrument makers, John Foulds was one of the millwrights, the second post remaining unfilled, and the post of time-keeper maker was also left vacant; Samuel Brook was the printer.

The third class, the honorary members, the "Men of Science and Gentlemen of Fame and Fortune", contained only two who had been members before; Joseph Priestly, who had joined in 1773, and Matthew Boulton, elected in 1780. New honorary members were Sir Joseph Banks, Colonel Samuel Bentham, Major Rennell and George Maxwell. Sir Joseph was the naturalist who in 1768 had accompanied Captain Cook on his voyage round the world; and was President of the Royal Society from 1778 until his death in 1820; he attended the meetings of the Society regularly for more than 20 years.

Colonel Bentham practised as an engineer and naval architect, and in 1791 had become the Inspector of Naval Works. He also attended regularly for many years, but Rennell and Maxwell soon dropped out.

The Society now consisted of eight first class members, eight honorary members in the second class and six in the third class. All had been selected and invited by the committee and elected by the members present at meetings. Of those not invited to join, the two most notable were Joseph Nickalls, a founder member of the Society who had been the President for the previous ten years, and Hodgkinson, who had joined in 1777 and was the Vice President from 1781. Both were acknowledged to be civil engineers in the 1791 list of members and had attended meetings regularly right up to the end of the 1792 session, but they were left out. Nickalls' earlier offence to Smeaton played a significant part in his exclusion. According to Mylne, although the incident "was done away with by an apology at the desire of the company and by the good nature of Mr. Smeaton, the remembrance of it had an effect on all present".

The embarrassment which their exclusion must have caused probably explains the abandonment of the offices of President and Vice President under the new constitution. Mylne as Treasurer remained the sole office holder until his death in 1811, and there were no more Presidents for nearly 50 years. There were others, too, who through regular attendance during the previous 12 months might have expected a place in the reformed Society. One was Holmes, the clockmaker, left out despite the provision for a time-keeper maker which remained unfilled. Also, Jardin, Marquand and Thomas were not admitted; they had not been described as civil engineers in the 1791 list of members.

A new Minute Book was bought for 10s 6d and a box to hold it under lock and key, which cost 4s. The summons card was approved, and Faden was asked to get it re-engraved. This time a motto was added: "Omnia in Numero, Pondere et Mensura". It is a quotation from the Apocrypha, the Wisdom of Solomon, chapter 2, verse 20, "Thou hast ordered all things in measure and number and weight".

The rules and regulations continued to be discussed. The article relating to voting by the members was questioned as to whether honorary members should be entitled to vote on all matters affecting the Society, and when put to a ballot, it was resolved that the members of all classes had the right to vote in common. An attempt was made to remove the distinction between the three classes of membership, but a decision was deferred to the next meeting and the proposal was then defeated. It was resolved, however, that the third class, the honorary members, would in future be re-named the "Second Class" and the "Artists" transposed to the third class. After these changes, Brook produced a booklet entitled "Rules and Regulations for the institution of the Society of Civil Engineers, London"; 250 copies were printed and each member was given one.

James Playfair, architect, a former member, was re-elected in May 1793, but he died early in the following year. Sir George Shuckburgh-Evelyn, the mathematician, was also elected. He was the MP for the county of Warwick from 1780 until his death. In 1798, at the Royal Society, of which he had been a Fellow since 1774, he described his experiments to establish an accurate standard for the English yard, and he employed Edward Troughton to construct a graduated brass bar which is now in the possession of the Royal Society. He was also experimenting to establish accurate standards of volume and weight. Perhaps he inspired the Society's new motto?

The 1793 session ended on Saturday, 15 June, and the next session began on Friday, 7 February 1794. Meetings reverted to fortnightly and henceforth were held on Fridays. In March the venue was changed from the York Tavern, Blackfriars, to the Crown and Anchor, Strand, which having been rebuilt in 1790, offered better accommodation. Mylne reported on 4 April that he had retrieved the books and papers of the Society relating to the period 1771–92, which were found at the Kings Head, Holborn; and for their recovery he had disbursed half a guinea. His action was approved.

The Crown and Anchor, Strand

From its foundation in 1771, the purpose of the Society had been to bring together engineers to dine together, to get to know each other better, and by doing so to avoid the hostility which sometimes arose when they were called upon to report on each others' work, or to oppose in Parliamentary Committees the schemes the clients of colleagues wished to promote. The renewed Society in 1793 was given an additional purpose. It was to be "a Society for promoting and communicating every branch of knowledge useful and necessary to the various and important branches of public and private works in civil engineering". It was still primarily a dining club, and the standing toasts of the original Society were carried on, namely, "The King and Constitution", "The Society of Civil Engineers" and "Absent Members". To those was added another, "To the Memory of Our Late Worthy Brother, John Smeaton".

The toast "Success to Waterworks, Public or Private, that contribute to the use, to the comfort or the happiness of mankind", and the sentiment "Damn the canals, sink the coal pits, blast the minerals, consume the manufactures and disperse the commerce of Great Britain and Ireland", were in use in the early days of the reformed Society, although the time of their introduction is unrecorded. They were undoubtedly in use before 1810 because in that year Humphry Davy proposed an alteration to the sentiment; instead of consuming the manufactures and dispersing the commerce, he proposed "Disperse the manufactures and consume the produce", but his proposed amendment did not find favour.

The accumulation of printed reports, memoranda and plans under Rules 9 and 10 became an important feature of the business of the Society. Jessop presented copies of his plans of canals and inland navigations upon which he had been engaged. When the 1794 session opened Rennie gave copies of several plans of canals with which he had been concerned. Mylne contributed copies of his plans and printed reports. Prints of the receiver and distributor invented by Foulds and installed at the London Bridge Waterworks were given by him, and at the next meeting he presented the drawings of his regulating air vessels. These gifts were recorded but there is no evidence of their being discussed.

Robert Welldon, a non-member, was invited as a visitor to describe his invention of a new lock for inland navigation, its main feature being economy in the flow of water particularly where the fall of the ground was too steep for conventional locks to be used.

Two new members were elected in February 1794, Captain Joseph Huddart as a "Member of the First Class" and Dr Charles Hutton an honorary member of the newly re-designated second class.

Huddart, who was born at Allonby, Cumberland, on 11 June 1741 (N.S.), on leaving school went to sea in a brig of a fish-curing firm run by his father, and he succeeded to a share in the business when his father died. He entered the service of the East India Company in 1771 and made several voyages to the East, surveying many of the ports he visited and the coasts along which he navigated, including, at home, the St George's Channel. He retired from the company's service in 1788 and was elected an Elder Brother of Trinity House in 1791. Having suffered an accident from a cable parting at sea, he invented an improved method of making rope, and went into the business of manufacturing cordage. He died in London on 19 August 1816, and was buried in the crypt of St Martins-in-the-Fields.

Charles Hutton was a mathematician, having been in early life a schoolmaster in his native Newcastle-upon-Tyne. He practised surveying and drew an accurate map of that city. He became the Professor of Mathematics at the Royal Military Academy, Woolwich, in 1773, winning the post in open competition. He was elected a Fellow of the Royal Society in the following year and for his papers in 1776–78 on "The Force of Exploded Gunpowder on the Velocities of Balls", he gained the Copley Medal. In 1779 he was appointed Foreign Secretary of the Royal Society.

The first meeting that Huddart and Hutton attended was the meeting held for the first time at the Crown and Anchor on 21 March 1794.

The following year Henry Eastburn, a former member of the Society, was re-admitted and William Chapman was elected, both as first class members; John Watté, a land surveyor was appointed in the third class.

Henry Eastburn became Smeaton's pupil in 1768 and was his assistant from 1776. He worked as resident engineer on the Basingstoke Canal under Jessop in 1792–93 and the following year he was surveying the rivers Derwent and Rye in East Yorkshire for the Earl Fitzwilliam. He went on to the Lancaster Canal and was in charge until 1798. Then, on Rennie's recommendation, he was the resident engineer for the construction of London Docks.

William Chapman, who was born in 1749, was a friend of James Watt and Matthew Boulton. He was the engineer of the Kildare Canal and consultant for the Grand Canal, in Ireland. He too worked under Rennie in the London Docks. In June, Chapman gave the Society copies of his printed report on the survey of a navigation from Newcastle to the Irish Channel, his reports on the harbour of Arklow, Ireland, and on the practicability of a navigation in the Vale of Avoca. He followed these in 1798, with a copy of his "Observations in the Various Systems of Canal Navigation", published in 1797.

Sir Joseph Banks was in the chair at the meeting on 27 February 1795, when there was a discussion about the reports and papers of the late John Smeaton, which Banks had recently acquired. Sir Joseph, who had bought the papers for a considerable sum, offered to make them freely available to the Society, provided the original documents were returned to him afterwards. Should they be published any profit would have to go to the heirs of Smeaton's estate, in accordance with the terms of their agreement with Sir Joseph at the time of purchase.

A committee was appointed to examine the reports and to consider whether they should be published. The committee members were Sir Joseph Banks, Chairman, Jessop, Captain Huddart, Mylne and Rennie. At their first meeting, Sir Joseph tabled a list of all the manuscripts, etc. in his possession. Dr Hutton was appointed editor and then seven volumes of reports were handed to him at the meeting in November. After studying them, he recommended that prior to their being prepared for publication copies be made of them all, and Mylne undertook to arrange this.

By December 1796 the first part of the proposed publication was ready for the printer. It was brought to the meeting by Dr Hutton and handed over to Brook. Mylne reported in May that the printing had proceeded so far that one volume, nearly one third of the work, would soon be ready. He therefore suggested that a first instalment of a sum of money be placed in the hands of Faden, the publisher on behalf of the committee, to pay the expenses of publishing, advertising, etc.: each member of the committee was asked to put up £40. Faden reported that Jeremiah Dixon, Smeaton's son-in-law, had offered certain copperplates in his possession which were for use in connection with the publication, and this offer was thankfully accepted.

At the opening meeting of the next session on 17 November 1797, Rennie read a letter he had received, addressed to the committee and dated 30 October, from Mary Dixon, Smeaton's daughter. In it she gave an intimate and personal account of her father's character and achievements. The letter was gratefully acknowledged and ordered to be printed in the first volume, after the more formal tribute to Smeaton which Dr Hutton had written.

The committee wished a portrait of Smeaton to appear in Volume 1 and Faden was asked to get one engraved. Mather Brown's portrait, which Alexander Aubert had commissioned in 1788, was chosen and engraved by William Bromley.

The draft preface, written by Mylne, was read at the meeting, amended and ordered to be reprinted; the title page was altered to ensure that the copyright was vested in the committee. The price to the public of Volume 1 was fixed at 18s. The bill for paper and printing amounted to £283 19s 0d which sum was owing to Brook; Faden was asked to pay him £100 out of the money in his hands, as part payment. Before the next meeting Brook had died, but Faden said that he had paid the money to the agent for Mrs Brook, the administratrix of her late husband's estate.

Volume 1 of Smeaton's reports, in a finished state ready for publication, was approved by the committee on 14 February 1798. It bore the title *"Reports of the Late John Smeaton FRS Made on Various Occasions in the Course of his Employment as A Civil Engineer"*. The reports were arranged in chronological order by subjects and about half of the reports were in Volume 1. It was published on 23 March, and the committee arranged for copies to be sent, on behalf of the Society, to each of Smeaton's daughters, Mary Dixon and Ann Brooke, and to Dr Hutton, the editor. A copy was also sent to John Holmes on account of his relationship to Smeaton.

By November, 89 copies had been sold at 18s each; and with the contributions of the committee members Faden had received altogether £280 2s 0d. The sum paid or due to Brook the printer was £395 15s 3d, leaving a deficit of £115 13s 3d, which did not include any sum due to Faden himself for his publishing costs. Then Rennie reported that he had received a proposal from Taylor, a bookseller of Holborn. Taylor offered to buy all the remaining copies of Volume 1, the prepared manuscripts for the second volume and Smeaton's drawings in the possession of Sir Joseph Banks which were suitable for illustrating both volumes. But in view of the several interests involved, namely, Sir Joseph as owner of the documents, the committee responsible for publication and the heirs of Smeaton's estate, it was decided not to accept this proposition, nor to enter into any contract where such varied interests were involved, in view of the difficulties that were likely to arise.

Two new members were admitted to the Society in 1795; in the first class, James Cockshutt, a former pupil and associate of Smeaton, who helped to design the first bar rolling mill used in the manufacture of wrought iron by Henry Cort's method. He was later the manager of Wortley Iron Works, Sheffield.

In the second class, Henry Oxenden was elected but never attended the meetings. Thomas Milne, the land surveyor, resigned, and a vacancy was declared in the third class. The following year, the Earl of Morton, John Lloyd, a barrister, and the Honourable Charles

FIRST CLASS.—Ordinary Members.

ORDINARY MEMBERS.

ORDINARY MEMBERS.

WILLIAM JESSOP,
ROBERT WHITWORTH,
JOHN RENNIE, F. R. S. Ed.
ROBERT MYLNE, F. R. S.
JAMES WATT, F. R. S.—L. and Ed.
JAMES GOLBORNE,
Sir THOMAS H. PAGE, Knt. F. R. S.
JOHN DUNCOMBE,
Captain JOSEPH HUDDART, F. R. S.
HENRY EASTBURNE,
WILLIAM CHAPMAN, M. R. I. A.
JAMES COCKSHUTT

SECOND CLASS.

The Right Hon. Sir JOSEPH BANKS, Bart. P. R. S. Knight of the Order of the Bath, &c.

Sir GEORGE A. SHUCKBURGH EVELYN, Bart. F. R. S.

MATHEW BOLTON, Esq; F. R. S.

General BENTHAM,

JOSEPH PRIESTLY, Esq;

Doctor CHARLES HUTTON, F. R. S.

HENRY OXENDON, Esq;

The Right Hon. the Earl of MORTON, F. R. S.

JOHN LLOYDD, Esq; F. R. S.

Right Hon. CHARLES GREVILLE, Esq; F. R. S.

THIRD CLASS.

WILLIAM FADEN, Geographer,

JESSE RAMSDEN, F. R. S. Instrument-Maker, &c.

JOHN TROUGHTON, Instrument-Maker, &c.

JOHN FOULDS, Mill-Wright, &c.

SAMUEL PHILLIPS, Engine-Maker,

SAMUEL BROOKE, Printer,

JOHN WATTE', Land-Surveyor, &c.

List of members, 1799

Greville, the mineralogist, were elected honorary members. All three attended the meetings of the Society regularly. George, 16th Earl of Morton, was the grandson of the 14th Earl, the scientist, mathematician and astronomer, who had succeeded the Earl of Macclesfield as President of the Royal Society in 1764 and had raised funds for Captain Cook's first voyage of discovery, in which Sir Joseph Banks had taken part. Although he had not inherited his grandfather's scientific and mathematical gifts, George was a very active member of the Society for 23 years, frequently taking the chair at meetings.

The imbalance between engineers and others which had led to reorganisation in 1792–93 had been corrected by the action of the committee in their selection of those they invited to join the reformed Society. Subsequent growth of the first class members was slow, as only engineers of established reputation were nominated and elected. The main expansion of membership came in the second class of honorary members as "Gentlemen of importance" were elected. The third class of "Artists, etc." could not grow, as its constitution was fixed and entry only permitted in a vacancy. For example, following the death of Samuel Brook his son, also Samuel, applied to succeed his father as printer to the Society. He was nominated and elected a member in the third class.

In order to prepare a new list of members for printing, a manuscript list was first compiled and attendance figures produced. Those members who had not attended after election or whose attendance had been allowed to lapse were written to and asked if they wished to pay their arrears of annual contributions and attend in future. After consideration and amendment of the list it was ordered to be printed in 1799 and was incorporated by Mylne in his preface to Smeaton's reports, Volume 1.

The second class of honorary members continued to expand. Jean Louis Barallier of Milford Haven, a government servant, formerly of the maritime service in Toulon, was elected in March 1798; Charles Hatchett, chemist, was admitted in May, and George Dance, RA, the architect, in December. Three more entered the following year: Captain William Mudge, who when the East India Company opened their engineering college at Addiscombe in 1809 was its first commandant and later became the Director of the Ordnance Survey; Richard Ellison, the MP for Lincoln; and Benjamin Count Rumford, one of the founders of the Royal Institution of Great Britain, which was established in 1799 "for the diffusion of knowledge, of inventions and scientific discoveries".

The Society continued its role in the promotion and communication of knowledge. Mylne brought to the meeting in May 1798 a book entitled "*Receuil de Plûsieurs Machines de nouvelle inventions, ouvrage posthume de M. Perault, à Paris 1700*". It described the construction of a bridge by putting cast iron frames together, and proposed such a bridge over the Seine at Sèvres. In discussion it was revealed that a bridge constructed on the same principles as M. Perault's had been erected over Virginia Water in Windsor Park prior to 1759, by direction of William Duke of Cumberland, but it had since been demolished.

Mylne also laid before the Society details of a number of bridges of large span in various parts of Switzerland, France and Italy, some of timber, some of stone. A letter which gave some interesting particulars of Smeaton's report on Walton Bridge came into Mylne's hands, and it was agreed to print it in Volume 2 of Smeaton's reports, when that volume should come to be undertaken.

Rennie produced a paper by Dr Ewart on the hot springs of Bath and their subterranean origins, and Faden presented a copy of his latest publication, a new edition of papers in the Royal Society's *Transactions* on the trigonometrical survey of Great Britain.

A print of the centring used in the construction of Westminster Bridge, the work of J. King, carpenter, was given by Mylne, who also produced a model of a circular wedge proposed for striking the centring, although it was not found practicable to use it in the event. Sir Joseph Banks conveyed, on behalf of the author, a copy of Reinhard Boltman's first volume of essays on hydraulic architecture which was in German.

Robert Whitworth, a member of long standing, who had served on the committee of reorganisation in 1792, died on 30 March 1799. He had attended meetings regularly for many years and made his last appearance in April 1797. In his obituary notice he was described as "one of the most able engineers in this country". In November 1800 Jesse Ramsden, the instrument maker, died and in the vacancy in the third class which this created, Peter Dolland was elected.

Alexander Aubert was elected in the second class in 1800. He was a great admirer of Smeaton and had been associated with him in 1787, when as chairman of the trustees of Ramsgate Harbour he involved Smeaton in the improvements of the port. In 1788 Aubert commissioned Mather Brown to paint Smeaton's portrait, which he gave to the Royal Society. This was the portrait, engraved by William Bromley in 1790, which appeared in Volume 1 of Smeaton's reports.

William Vaughan was elected a member in the second class in February 1801. He was born on 22 September 1752, and after leaving school entered his father's firm of London merchants. He became a director of the Royal Exchange Assurance Corp. and during the naval mutiny at the Nore in 1797 was one of a committee convened in the city to help restore peace. From 1793 to 1797 he published a series of tracts advocating the construction of docks for the Port of London and gave evidence for the Parliamentary Bill to establish wet docks in London. He gave copies of these tracts to the Society.

Sir Thomas Hyde Page resigned in March 1802, saying that public business and attention to his private affairs had prevented his attending meetings in recent times and would probably continue to do so. His record showed that he had not attended for upwards of two years. At the same time it was brought to notice that John Watté, land surveyor, had not attended for many years; John Duncombe had not been present since March 1796; Jean Louis Barallier had never attended, although elected in 1798; John Foulds, the millwright, had been absent for three years and Dr Hutton for four. All except Barallier were removed from the list of members.

Jeremiah Dixon, as the representative of Smeaton's family, sent Faden two boxes containing 34 copperplates for use in further publications of Smeaton's reports. The Society welcomed this gift which, it was said, would enable the committee to proceed without delay to publish the second volume and ultimately to form a uniform quarto complete edition, with illustrations, of all Smeaton's written works, including his reports on the Eddystone Lighthouse, Spurn Point Lighthouse and Ramsgate Harbour.

The 1803 session opened on 3 December 1802, and in a letter Mrs Brook complained that the remaining copies of Volume 1 of Smeaton's reports which were stored in her warehouse were not only inconvenient to her but liable to injury and damage. She asked that they be removed to some more proper place. No action was taken immediately, and in July, Samuel Brook, jnr, wrote saying that the copies were spoiling fast and were a great inconvenience. He also wished to know to whom he must apply for the payment of the balance of the account. The last instalment he had received was £50 in July 1799. Mylne offered to take over the remaining copies of Volume 1 and undertook to remove them to a place of safe custody. But it was July 1806 before Faden could make another payment.

At the meeting in May 1803 it was proposed to have engravings made of all the relevant drawings etc., the property of Sir Joseph Banks, required to illustrate the reports in Volume 1 as an addition to it. The eight members present at the meeting, Rennie, Mylne, Jessop, Faden, Aubert, Dolland, Cockshutt and Vaughan all agreed to subscribe. Sir Joseph Banks and John Lloyd added their names later. Each agreed to pay at least five guineas: some paid twice as much and others joined in afterwards. In all £115 was raised.

There were more additions to the Society's records. Vaughan presented a new map of Russia showing the inland navigations, with plans of the canals depicted in the margins. Rennie presented a book containing reports and maps of the harbours of Dublin which he had received from the Director-General of Inland Navigations in Ireland.

Four more honorary members were elected in the second class in 1804; the Reverend Dr Nevil Maskelyne, the Astronomer Royal; Sir John Morris, of Place Mount, Swansea, an industrialist; John Hamilton, Viscount Kirkwall and Colonel Thomas Richard Beaumont, MP for Northumberland.

Sir George Shuckburgh-Evelyn, who had attended meetings regularly from the time of his election in 1793 until 1802, died on 11 August 1804. Jean Louis Barallier, who had been elected in 1798, attended for the first time on 1 February 1805, when Charles Greville introduced him. Thereafter he was very regular in attendance.

William Parsons and the Right Honourable Lord Dundas were elected in 1805 after which a new list of members was compiled and ordered to be printed. There were nine first class members, 22 honorary members in the second class, and five members plus two vacancies in the third class.

At the meeting on 21 February 1806, Mylne reported the cost of publishing Smeaton's reports and recommended another subscription of five guineas each. Four of the five members present put down their names and six more subscribed at the next meeting; others joined in later. Before the session closed in July, Faden had paid Brook £26 5s 0d out of the subscription money he held, and £13 2s 6d being the proceeds of sales of the book. During the session four more members were admitted to the second class: Lovell Edgeworth, Colonel Mark Beaufoy and two MPs, the Honourable George Knox and William Smith.

When the 1807 session started on 19 December 1806, Mylne was indisposed and the minutes were written by Faden. At the next meeting no one but Mylne turned up. His entry in the minutes reads "Present, Mr Mylne, solus cum solo. Mr Mylne paid his annual subscription 10s 6d and collected from one member 8s 0d. Bill £1 8s 6d advance by Mr Mylne 10s 0d".

The annual subscription had been 10s 6d ever since the reform of the Society in 1793, but it was increased to 18s 6d, at the beginning of the 1809 session: members attending the meetings contributed 8s towards the cost of their dinners as they had done before. From February 1810 the annual subscription was raised to three guineas, but members were no longer required to contribute separately to the dinner bill.

Dr William Herschel, the astronomer, and Humphry Davy, Professor of Chemistry at the Royal Institution and Secretary of the Royal Society, were elected honorary members in 1808. In the following year Joseph Whidbey was elected; he had carried out coastal surveys while accompanying Captain George Vancouver on his voyage round the world, and held the appointment of Master Intendent at Woolwich Dockyard. For many years he had worked under Rennie on the construction of Plymouth Breakwater. When John Troughton died in 1807 the vacancy in the third class for an instrument maker was not filled immediately: Peter Dollond remained the sole instrument maker. In May 1810 George Dollond and Edward Troughton, John's younger brother, were both elected.

The publication of Volume 2 of Smeaton's reports was discussed in March 1808, when Mylne proposed that a further subscription be raised for the purpose.

Sir Joseph Banks was asked for permission to have copies made of all the drawings and plans in his possession that would be needed to illustrate both Volume 1, already published, and the projected volumes. Rennie approached Messrs Longman, Hurst & Co. to see if they would publish the remaining volumes and the illustrations for Volume 1. In March 1809 he was able to report progress. Longman Hurst would undertake all the expenses of the next two volumes of the reports, including the engravings for these and Volume 1, provided the copyright was theirs. Sir Joseph Banks obtained a release from his undertakings that any profit from publication of the reports would go to the heirs of Smeaton's estate.

Longmans offered to give the Society 30 copies of the reports they published, but required the Society to give them 500 copies of Volume 1. The matter was referred to the committee set up to publish the first volume and it was agreed that the committee's decision would be binding on the Society. The committee was asked to obtain 40 copies rather than 30 from Longmans "in case Mr Rennie shall be able to improve the bargain". The arrangements were concluded satisfactorily, and Mylne delivered 120 copies of Volume 1 to Longman Hurst in February; additional copies would have to be printed.

Two more honorary members were elected in 1811; John George Children, one of the librarians at the British Museum, and Davies Giddy, MP for Bodmin, who, although not an engineer, had studied the theory of suspension bridges and criticised Telford's Menai Straits Bridge in Parliament. He adopted the surname Gilbert in 1817.

When the Society was reorganised in 1793 and written rules were adopted, members of the first class were authorised to use the style and title of "Member of the Society of Civil Engineers", and many did so. A publication "Properties of a New Invention" by John Duncombe, was brought to the attention of the meeting in February 1811, because in it Duncombe described himself as a member of the Society, although he had been struck off the list in 1802 as he had not attended any meetings for six years. The Secretary was instructed to point out to him that he was not entitled to describe himself as a member.

Robert Mylne died on 5 May 1811. He was the last of the founders and had played a leading part in the reorganisation of 1793. Afterwards he was the holder of the only office, that of Treasurer. He had served the Society well for more than 40 years. As architect and builder, his work included many town and country houses. He was the engineer of bridges and canals and worked on the drainage of the Fens; his Eau Brink Cut near Lynn was completed by Rennie in 1817. Early in 1811, Mylne had resigned as engineer of the New River Company in favour of his son, William Chadwell Mylne. At the meeting of the Society which followed the announcement of Robert's death, the admission of his son to membership was proposed by Rennie and seconded by Captain Huddart and Whidbey; he was elected on 14 June, the last meeting of the session.

Robert had been appointed Surveyor of St Paul's Cathedral in October 1766, and held the post until his death. He was buried in the crypt there. After the announcement of his death, in the toast to "the memory of our late worthy brother . . . ." Mylne's name was added to that of Smeaton.

Chapter Three

1812–1840

Following Mylne's death William Vaughan acted as Treasurer, but the leading role in the Society was played by John Rennie. Not only was he a member of long standing but in his engineering practice he had achieved a pre-eminent position and was publicly recognised as the leading engineer of the day. He was the youngest of four sons of James Rennie of Phantassie, East Lothian, where he was born on 7 June 1761. On leaving the parish school he joined Andrew Meickle, millwright at Linton, and after two years went to Dunbar High School. In 1780 he entered Edinburgh University where he studied natural philosophy and chemistry, remaining there until 1783. He then worked as a millwright on his own account. In 1784 he crossed the border and toured the industrial towns of NW England and the Midlands "to enlarge his knowledge". He visited the Soho Factory at Birmingham and was invited by James Watt to supervise the machinery for the new Albion Mills, Blackfriars, designed by Samuel Wyatt, for which Boulton and Watt were building the steam engines. This occupied Rennie for the next four years. In 1791 he set up his own practice in Holland Street, Blackfriars, and as well as the manufacture of machinery Rennie also engaged in the planning and construction of many important public works.

Although Mylne had been active in the preparation of Smeaton's papers for publication, it was Rennie who dealt with Longman & Co. who now had publication firmly in their hands. There were illustrations for Volume 1 and its reprinting; the publication of two more volumes of the reports; publication of the miscellaneous papers in the *Philosophical Transactions* of the Royal Society, which would constitute Volume 4, and a new edition of the Eddystone Lighthouse report, first published during Smeaton's lifetime.

Approval was given in January 1812 for the printing of Volumes 2 and 3 of the reports, and Longmans were recommended to produce 750 copies. Copies of the reports were sent to Smeaton's daughters, Mary Dixon and Ann Brooke, as in the case of Volume 1; copies were

LIST of the SOCIETY of CIVIL ENGINEERS,

LONDON, FEBRUARY, M.DCCC.XII.

FIRST CLASS.—Ordinary Members.

James Watt, F.R.S., L. & E.	Heathfield, Birmingham.
William Jessop	Butterley, Derbyshire.
John Rennie, F.R.S., F.A.S. & F.R.S.E., &c.	Stamford-street, Christ Church, Surrey.
Captain Joseph Huddart, F.R.S.	Highbury-terrace, Islington.
William Chapman, M.R.I.A.	
James Golborne	Ely, Cambridgeshire.
James Cockshutt	Mr. Maud's, Mincing Lane.
William Mylne	New River Head, Islington.

SECOND CLASS.—Honorary Members.

Right Hon. Sir Joseph Banks, Bart., K.B., P.R.S.	Soho-square.
The Earl of Morton, K.T., F.R.S.	Park-street, Grosvenor-square.
The Right Hon. Lord Dundas, F.R.S., &c.	Arlington-street.
Benjamin Count of Rumford, F.R.S., &c.	Munich, Germany.
Charles Hatchett, Esq, F.R.S. L. & E., &c.	Mount Clare, Wimbledon.
John Lloyd, Esq., F.R.S., F.A.S., &c.	Wygfair, St. Asaph.
Dr. William Herschell, F.R.S.	Slough.
G. L. Barallier, Esq., Assistant Surveyor of the Navy	Upper Eaton-street, Pimlico.
Joseph Priestley, Esq.	Bradford, Yorkshire.
William Vaughan, Esq.	Dunster-court, Mincing-lane.
John Morris, Esq.	Swansea.
William Parsons, Esq., F.R.S.	Sloane-street.
Richard Lovell Edgworth, M.R.I.A.	Edgeworth's Town, Ireland.
Colonel Mark Beaufoy, F.R.S.	Hackney Walk.
Joseph Whidbey, Esq., F.R.S.	Plymouth Dock.
Humphry Davy, Esq., F.R.S.	Royal Institution.
John George Children, Esq., F.R.S.	Upper King-street, Bloomsbury.
William Smith, Esq., M.P., F.R.S.	Queen-square Place
Davies Giddy, Esq., M.P., F.R.S. & F.L.S.	Hollis-street.
Thomas Murdoch, Esq., F.R.S.	Portland-place.
John Barrow, Esq., F.R.S.	Admiralty.

THIRD CLASS.

Mr. George Dollond, } Opticians	St. Paul's Church Yard.
Mr. Peter Dolland, }	
Mr. Edw. Troughton, F.R.S., Mat. Inst. Maker	Fleet-street.
Mr. William Faden, Geographer	Charing Cross.

List of members, 1812

also sent to the Royal Society, the British Museum, the Advocates' Library in Edinburgh, the universities of Oxford and Cambridge, the colleges at Edinburgh and Glasgow, and the Royal Irish Academy. Members of the Society who had subscribed seven guineas or more were given copies from the volumes belonging to the Society, and those who had subscribed five guineas qualified for copies if they paid another two guineas.

Longmans pointed out that the papers in the *Philosophical Transactions* occupied 300 pages and ten plates; if they were to print them in the same number of pages, the cost of 500 copies would be £212, but if they could have the use of the copies of the Royal Society, the expense would be about 80 guineas less. It was decided to proceed with publication of the papers, and Vaughan, the acting Treasurer, was authorised to apply the funds in his hands to this purpose. Publication of the new edition of the Eddystone Lighthouse report was discussed in January 1812, and Longmans offered to give the Society £100 for every 250 copies sold. This proposal was accepted, on condition that the Society be given two copies (later increased to four when instructions to proceed were given in April).

Early in 1812 there were two more additions to the members in the second class; Thomas Murdoch and Sir John Barrow, the Secretary of the Admiralty. A corrected list of members of the Society was produced by Rennie; it was approved and ordered to be printed.

Longmans wrote in May 1813 indicating that they were ready to publish the miscellaneous papers (Volume 4 of Smeaton's works) if the Society would procure from the Royal Society the plates which were used in their publication. The Society undertook to do this. Longmans then asked for an advance of £94 towards the expense of publication, to which the Society agreed.

Rennie produced the preface to Volume 4, which he had been asked to write, at the meeting on 8 July 1814, and it was read by Davies Giddy and approved. Vaughan was authorised to pay Longmans the amount agreed. The Society received a copy of the publication in February 1815, and when it was produced at the meeting in March the purchase of a large chest was approved for holding the books and other archives of the Society.

Mary Dixon asked the Society if she could have 50 copies of Smeaton's portrait, and of the vignette and section of the Eddystone Lighthouse, as reproduced in the reports. Before conceding this the Society wished to find out the cost. Longmans agreed to give Mrs Dixon the plates she wanted without any expense to the Society.

With an annual subscription of three guineas the Society was just about paying its way. In the 1811 session the dinner bills added up to

£70 14s and the income was £69 6s 0d. The following year, income
exceeded expenditure by £13, and in 1813 by £12 2s 7d. In 1814 the
surplus was only £2 17s 6d. There was extra expenditure on the chest
in 1815. The money subscribed for the publications was kept
separate.

William Jessop, a member since 1773 and one of the committee of
reorganisation in 1793, died aged 69 in November 1814. His father,
Josias, was a shipwright at Plymouth who had maintained the old
Eddystone Lighthouse, and after it was destroyed had become
Smeaton's assistant in building the new one. Smeaton took William as
a pupil and when his pupillage was over William became his assistant.
Canals were Jessop's main activity when he started on his own, and
he was the engineer for the Ellesmere Canal on which Telford was the
resident engineer until 1795, when Telford took over as engineer with
Jessop as consultant. When in 1799 the West India Dock Co. was
formed, Jessop was appointed engineer. The docks were completed in
1805. In 1799 a plan for a canal between London and Portsmouth was
mooted, but a horse-drawn tramway, favoured by Jessop and
supported by Rennie, was proposed as an alternative. The Surrey
Iron Railway Co., as it was called, appointed Jessop as Chief
Engineer, and the section from Wandsworth to Croydon was
completed in 1803; it was the first public railway in Britain.

Jessop was one of the founders of the Butterley Ironworks, a
foundry and mechanical engineering works which, after his death,
was run by his younger son, William. Josias, his elder son, succeeded
his father as engineer to the Bristol Docks, which were William's last
major work. In 1803, William Jessop, snr, had been appointed as
consultant to the Caledonian Canal where he again worked with
Telford, visiting it annually until 1812. He died at Butterley Hall,
Derbyshire, where the last nine years of his life had been spent. Josias
was proposed for membership in the first class by Rennie, seconded
by Lloyd and Faden, and was elected on 19 November 1813.

There were two elections of honorary members in April 1812:
Major General John Garstin of the Bengal Engineers, and the new
Astronomer Royal, John Pond, who had succeeded Dr Nevil
Maskelyne in February 1811. Pond was born in London in 1767; at
the age of 16 he went up to Trinity College, Cambridge, where he
read chemistry, but after having to leave due to ill health, he travelled
abroad, making astronomical observations in many countries. He
settled in Westbury, Somerset, in 1798 and there erected an
altazimuth instrument, made for him by Edward Troughton. He
moved to London in 1807 and occupied himself with practical
astronomy.

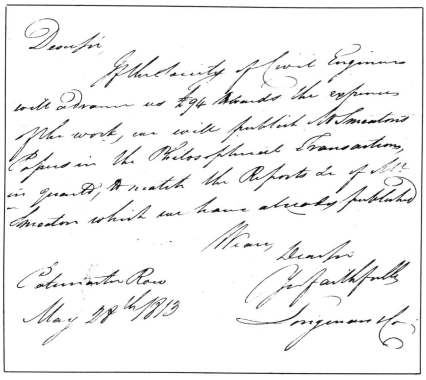

Publication of miscellaneous papers, letter from Longmans

The procedure for the admission of new members was, by now, well established and was strictly enforced. A candidate had to be proposed at a meeting by a member and seconded by two others; the details were recorded in the Minutes. A notice was put up in the meeting room at a subsequent meeting and at the next opportunity a ballot took place. After his election the new member was introduced to the assembled company at the next convenient meeting.

Robert Stevenson applied for membership of the Society in a letter brought before the meeting on 19 May 1815. He had succeeded his step-father, Thomas Smith, as Surveyor to the Northern Lighthouse Board. In response to his letter Stevenson was informed of the qualifications for membership and the procedure to be followed, but it was some years before he became a member.

A change of venue was suggested. The closing meeting of the 1816 session was held at the Freemasons Tavern, but when the next session opened in February 1817, dinners were resumed at the Crown and Anchor where the members had been well served for 23 years.

Crown & Anchor Tavern March 7th 1817

At a Meeting of the Society of Civil Engineers

The Earl of Morton in the Chair

Lewis Gibbot Esq
Arthur Rafer
William Vaugham
James Sprya
William Smith
William Hughes
William Chapman
John Rennie

Cash brought forward	£25..6..	Paid
William Chapman Jun.d	3..3	Paid
William Vaugham	3..3	
	£31..10	
Arthur Rafer	3..3	
	£34..13	

£5..--
5..15
£10..15

March 7, 1817

Bread & Cheer — 4..5
Dinner — 2..0
Claret Wine — 7..
Sherry — 1..6
H.t Beer & Ale — 3..
Port — 1..11
Sherry — 14..
Glass —
Servants Dinner — 1..6
Tea — 17..
Soda — 1..

Wine £5..0..6
5..1..6
£3..15..0

Dinner at the Crown and Anchor, 7 March 1817

The aim of the Society from its inception was to bring together practising engineers to share their experience and get to know each other better. The advancement of knowledge was an ancillary purpose, which began with Smeaton's and Walford's gifts of papers and reports in 1782 and was formally adopted by the reformed Society in 1793, after which there was a flood of reports and plans. By 1817 the flow had virtually dried up but no doubt the discussions at the dinner table continued to be a valuable exchange between experienced senior engineers and their knowledgeable friends.

In 1818 there was a new development. A group of eight young aspiring engineers, faced with limited opportunities for enlarging their knowledge, met at the invitation of Henry Robinson Palmer, at Kendal's Coffee House in Fleet Street. Their meeting led to the founding of the Institution of Civil Engineers. Its purpose was the acquisition of knowledge in the civil engineering profession: it was not to be a dining club, but a society solely devoted to the advancement of knowledge in the field of engineering. It catered for the young. Initially membership was restricted to those under the age of 35, and the average age of its founders was 25 years—Palmer was only 23 at the time—very different from the eminent engineers of the Society.

The Institution struggled for the first two years of its existence, but its success was assured when in 1820 Thomas Telford accepted the invitation to become its first President. The Institution met weekly on Tuesdays from the first Tuesday in November until the end of the parliamentary session. Its meetings did not clash with the Society's fortnightly meetings on Fridays. In January 1820 the upper age limit for election to membership of the Institution was abolished and a class of Corresponding Members introduced for those who lived and worked more than 10 miles from London. This opened the door to members of the Society, but it was some years before simultaneous membership of both organisations became commonplace.

In April 1821, Longman, Hurst & Co. wrote two letters to Rennie. In the first, dated 9 April, the firm proposed to sell off the remaining copies of Smeaton's Eddystone Lighthouse report and give the proceeds to the Society, unless it was in excess of their commitment to pay £100 for 250 copies. In the second, dated 23 April, they abandoned all idea of paying the Society anything, but asked for permission to dispose of the copies in any way they thought fit. The Society sought the views of the heirs of Smeaton's estate, and in May the solicitors acting for them gave their consent. Longmans were informed that the Society did not object to their proposal.

On 4 October 1821, John Rennie died. He had settled in London in 1791, and in addition to manufacturing machinery he developed his practice in engineering works. The Kennet and Avon Canal was his first project, but other canals followed: the Rochdale, the Lancaster and a revision of the plans for the Royal Canal of Ireland. He was also engaged in the drainage of the Fens, the construction of London Docks, East and West India Docks, Ramsgate Harbour and the Royal Dockyards at Sheerness and Chatham. But he is best remembered for his Thames bridges; Waterloo Bridge, Southwark Bridge and London Bridge, which was completed after his death by his younger son John; John also completed his father's other major work, the Plymouth Breakwater.

Rennie died at Stamford Street, London, after a short illness, and like Robert Mylne was buried in St Paul's Cathedral. After his death the family interests were divided; the factory for the manufacture of machinery, under the name of J & G Rennie, was managed by George, the elder son; John inherited his father's construction engineering practice, continuing the work in hand. The Society, at its first meeting of the 1822 session, mourned the death of the Treasurer and the loss they had sustained, paying tribute to him.

At the next meeting William Chadwell Mylne was invited to accept the office of Treasurer. He was Robert Mylne's second son, born in April 1781, who had assisted his father in setting out the Eau Brink Cut and worked on the Gloucester and Berkeley Canal. In 1804 he was appointed assistant engineer to the New River Company and succeeded his father as engineer in 1811. Between 1811 and 1821 his main works included the Colchester Waterworks and surveys of the Thames and Portsmouth Harbour. Abroad he was engaged in engineering works in and around Paris.

Membership numbers had declined and how to reverse this trend was under discussion at the meeting in March 1822. Josias Jessop, who was absent from the meeting due to a severe cold, expressed through Mylne his sincere regret at not being able to attend. He hoped the Society would rally and promised his active support. When the next meeting was summoned, each member was asked to come prepared with the names of those they would like to see admitted to membership. A spate of elections followed. George and John Rennie, the sons of the late Treasurer, and James Watt, jnr, who had followed in his father's footsteps in Boulton and Watt, Birmingham, were elected as first class members. Joseph Whidbey was transferred from the second class to the first. In the second class of honorary members, there were nine admissions: Daniel Moore, scientist; Peter Ewart, Rennie's former assistant, who had joined Boulton and Watt; Francis

John Smeaton

Robert Mylne

James Watt

John Rennie

LIST

OF

Che Society of Civil Engineers.

INSTITUTED BY JOHN SMEATON, F.R.S., ANNO. 1793.

FIRST CLASS.—ORDINARY MEMBERS.

WILLIAM CHAPMAN, M.R.I.A.	Surry-street.
WILLIAM CHADWELL MYLNE	New River Head, London.
JOSIAH JESSOP	Adelphi.
JAMES WATT, F.R.S.	Aston Hall, Birmingham.
GEORGE RENNIE, F.R.S.	Royal Mint.
JOHN RENNIE, F.R.S.	Stamford-street.
JOSEPH WHIDBEY, F.R.S., F.L.S.	Plymouth.

SECOND CLASS.—HONORARY MEMBERS.

DAVIES GILBERT, Esq., V.P. & T.R.S., F.S.A., F.L.S.	Bridge-street.
WILLIAM VAUGHAN, F.R.S., F.L.S.	Mincing-lane.
Colonel MARK BEAUFOY, F.R.S, F.L.S.	Bushy Heath.
M. RAPER, Esq., F.R.S., F.S.A.	Wimpole-street.
Sir HUMPHREY DAVY, Bart., P.R.S., F.R.S. Ed., M.R.I., M.R.I.A., F.S.A....	Lower Grosvenor-street.
DANIEL MOORE, Esq., F.R.S., F.S.A., F.L.S., M.R.I.	Lincoln's Inn New-square.
PETER EWART, Esq., M.P.S.M.	Manchester.
FRANCIS CHANTREY, Esq., F.R.S., R.A., F.S.A. ...	Pimlico.
HENRY BROWN, Esq., F.R.S., F.S.A.	Portland Place.
CHARLES BABBAGE, Esq., F.R.S., L. & E. Reg.Acad. Monach. Society	Devonshire-street.
General ROWLEY, F.R.S., Roy. Eng....	Queen's-square, Bloomsbury.
Major COLBY, F.R.S., Roy. Eng.	Tower.
JOHN BARTON, Esq., F.R.S.	Royal Mint.
Sir R. SEPPINGS, Knt., F.R.S.	Somerset Place.
FRANCIS BAILEY, Esq., F.R.S.	Verulam Buildings, Gray's Inn.
Captain BEAUFORT, F.R.S.	Manchester-street.
JOHN TAYLOR, Esq.	Bedford-row.

THIRD CLASS.

EDWARD TROUGHTON, F.R.S., Mat. Inst. Maker ...	Fleet-street.
GEORGE DOLLOND, F.R.S., Optician	St. Paul's Churchyard.

London, July, 1823.

List of members, 1823

Chantrey, RA, the sculptor; Henry Browne, astronomer; Charles Babbage, mathematician; Major General John Rowley, RE; Major Thomas Colby, Director of the Ordnance Survey; John Barton, Deputy Controller of the Royal Mint; and Sir Robert Seppings, naval architect. Troughton and Dolland, the only survivors in the third class, continued in membership but were no longer described as honorary members.

In the drive to restore the Society's success the number of meetings was changed from fortnightly on Fridays to monthly on the first Wednesday of the month during the session of Parliament, and the subscription was reduced from three guineas to one. Dinners were to be arranged to cost no more than 5s per head, and the members attending were to pay 9s each, any expense in excess of 9s being borne by the general fund of the Society. In May members voted in favour of reverting to meeting fortnightly, and the first and third Wednesdays of the month were chosen.

At some time after the death of John Rennie the traditional toast at dinner, which followed "Absent Members", was altered once more: it became "To the memory of our late worthy brothers, Smeaton, Mylne, Watt and Rennie".

The long established practice of proposing and seconding candidates at one meeting and balloting at the next or a subsequent one, which had not been observed in the spate of elections on 26 March 1822, was resumed in 1823, but henceforth one seconder sufficed instead of two. Francis Baily, astronomer, and John Taylor were proposed and seconded on 3 April 1823 and elected as honorary members on 7 May. Before the session ended, Captain Francis Beaufort, Hydrographer of the Navy, was also elected; he was the inventor of the Beaufort Scale for recording the strength of the wind at sea. A revised list of members was prepared in July; Davies Gilbert arranged for the copperplate to be brought up to date and the list printed.

At the beginning of the 1824 session the venue was changed from the Crown and Anchor, where the Society had been meeting for 30 years, to the Freemasons Tavern, Great Queen Street, Lincolns Inn Fields. During 1824 there were more additions to the membership. James Walker, already an active member of the Institution of Civil Engineers, was proposed in March and elected on 7 April as a first class member of the Society. Philip Taylor, the brother of John, and John Millington were elected in the second class at the same meeting. Captain Edward Sabine, RA, and Charles Stokes of Gray's Inn were elected before the end of the session, and another list of members was compiled.

When the next session opened on 16 February 1825 there was a change in the rules. Ballotting would in future be held on the second meeting after the candidate had been proposed and seconded; a single black ball would exclude any person from membership and the number of honorary members would in future be limited to 24. These changes were both proposed and decided at the meeting on 16 February which nine members, including Mylne and both Rennies, attended. At the next meeting it was proposed that no new regulation or alteration of the rules should be valid unless it was proposed at one meeting and decided upon at a subsequent meeting. A decision on this proposal was deferred until 16 March, and it was then approved. At the March meeting one candidate for membership was black-balled. George Rennie and William Mylne were asked to examine and report on the current rules and to make suggestions, if found desirable, for their improvement. The session ended with the election of William Jessop, Josias' younger brother, as a first class member and William Woolrych Whitmore, the MP for Bridgenorth, as an honorary member.

There were times when newly elected members failed to attend meetings once they were elected. There were difficulties for those residing at a distance, whose business did not bring them to London during the sessions of the Society; they could be excused and by custom were not required to pay the annual subscription. But in April 1826 a new rule was adopted which required all newly elected members residing in London, to attend a meeting within 12 months of the day of their election and to pay their dues: otherwise their membership would be cancelled.

Arrears of subscription were a problem; the accounts for the 1826 session showed money owing for every year from 1823, and although a payment of three guineas reduced the debt in 1826, it left 13 guineas still unpaid.

George Rennie proposed that the annual subscription be raised from one guinea to 40s and the higher subscription was collected for the 1827 session, increasing the income to £56 3s 6d. Expenditure amounted to £38 9s 0d, which included the cost of printing the lists of members and 300 summons cards at a cost of 15s. A new Minute Book, bound in plain calf and lettered, cost 13s 6d, but the main expenditure was on the tavern bills.

In that year, when two more members were elected, the designation First Class was dropped and James Jardine, engineer of the Edinburgh Water Co., and Robert Stevenson, also from Edinburgh, were described as Ordinary Members. Stevenson was born in Glasgow in 1772. His father died when he was two, and his mother married again when he was 16. He entered the office of his step-father, Thomas Smith, engineer to the newly constituted Northern Lighthouse Board, and in 1769 was taken into partnership. Stevenson succeeded Smith and served the Commissioners of Northern Lighthouses for nearly 40 years, not only constructing the lighthouses but also designing the lanterns and optical systems. The Bell Rock Lighthouse was his best known achievement.

In the same session Captain Basil Hall, RN, Captain Chapman, RA, and Lieut. Col. Charles William Pasley, RE, were elected honorary members. Charles Pasley, born in 1780, came from Eskdale, Dumfrieshire. In 1796 he joined the Royal Military Academy, Woolwich, and was commissioned in the Royal Artillery but he transferred to the Royal Engineers the following year. After active service in Spain and in the Low Countries he became the Director of Field Instruction at Chatham.

Francis Giles became a member in February 1828. He was a surveyor who taught John Rennie surveying and afterwards worked for him and for Thomas Telford. He surveyed the line for Marc Brunel's Thames Tunnel, and his route for the London and Birmingham Railway, through Rugby and Coventry, was the one adopted. He was the engineer for the tidal docks at Southampton and for the London and Southampton Railway until he handed over to Joseph Locke. Captain Pringle, RE, and Joseph Portlock, both of the Ordnance Survey, and Frederick Page were made honorary members in 1829.

Another list of members was printed in 1830. In this the engineers were described as "ordinary members", the rest were listed as "honorary members", no longer described as first, second and third classes.

When the 1831 session began on 19 January it was decided to revert to monthly meetings, this time in the third week of the month. This meant there were five meetings in the session compared with 11 fortnightly meetings in 1830. This led to a noticeable improvement in the numbers attending.

With the annual subscription still at £2 and expenditure curtailed, income exceeded outgoings, leaving a handsome balance in the Treasurers' hands at the end of the session. In consequence the subscription was reduced to £1 in 1832. In the period 1831–32 two more engineers were elected, bringing the number of ordinary members to twelve. William Cubitt came from Norfolk but had moved to London in 1826 and established his engineering practice there. William Tierney Clark was apprenticed to a millwright in Bristol and then worked at the Coalbrookdale Ironworks until 1808.

LIST

1830

OF THE

SOCIETY OF CIVIL ENGINEERS,

INSTITUTED BY JOHN SMEATON, F.R.S.

ANNO MDCCXCIII.

ORDINARY MEMBERS.

WILLIAM CHAPMAN, M.R.I.A.	Newcastle.
WILLIAM CHADWELL MYLNE, F.R.S.	New River Head, London.
JOSEPH WHIDBEY, F.R.S. F.L.S.	Plymouth.
GEORGE RENNIE, F.R.S.	Whitehall-place.
JOHN RENNIE, F.R.S.	Whitehall-place.
JAMES WALKER, F.R.S.L. & E.	Limehouse.
WILLIAM JESSOP	Butterley Hall, Derbyshire.
——— JARDINE	Edinburgh.
ROBERT STEVENSON	Edinburgh.
FRANCIS GILES	Salisbury-street, Strand.

HONORARY MEMBERS.

DAVIES GILBERT, Esq. P. & T.R.S. F.S.A. F.L.S. & F.G.S.	Bridge-street.
EDWARD TROUGHTON, Esq. F.R.S.	Fleet-street.
GEORGE DOLLOND, Esq. F.R.S.	St. Paul's Church-yard.
JAMES WATT, Esq. F.R.S.	Aston Hall, Birmingham.
PETER EWART, Esq. M.P.S.M.	Manchester.
FRANCIS CHANTREY, Esq. F.R.S. R.A. F.S.A.	Pimlico.
HENRY BROWNE, Esq. F.R.S. F.S.A.	Portland-place.
CHARLES BABBAGE, Esq. M.A. F.R.S.L. & E. M.R.I.A. Reg. Acad. Monach. Society	Devonshire-street.
JOHN TAYLOR, Esq. F.R.S. & P.G.S.	Bedford-row.
Lieut. Colonel COLBY, F.R.S.L. & E. M.R.I.A. F.G.S. Roy. Eng.	Tower.
JOHN BARTON, Esq. F.R.S.	Royal Mint.
Sir R. SEPPINGS, Knt. F.R.S.	Somerset-place.
FRANCIS BAILY, Esq. F.R.S. F.L.S. & F.G.S.	Tavistock-place.
Captain BEAUFORT, F.R.S.	Manchester-street.
Captain SABINE, F.R.S.	Portland-place.
CHARLES STOKES, Esq. F.R.S.	Gray's-Inn.
W. WOOLRYCH WHITMORE, Esq. M.P.	Bury-street, St. James's.
Captain BASIL HALL, R.N.	
Colonel PASLEY, Roy. Eng.	Chatham.
Captain CHAPMAN, Roy. Art.	
Captain PRINGLE, Roy. Eng.	Tower.
FREDERICK PAGE, Esq.	Hungerford.
JOSIAH E. PORTLOCK, Esq.	Ordnance Map Office, Tower.

List of members, 1830

John Rennie employed him at his works in Blackfriars until in 1811 he became the engineer of the Thames and Medway Canal. His practice involved several suspension bridges, including those at Hammersmith, Marlow and over the Arun. He designed and built the suspension bridge over the Danube joining Buda and Pest.

There were no more admissions until 1835, when three engineers were elected, Bryan Donkin, Joshua Field and James Simpson: all three, like Walker and Cubitt, were senior members of the Institution of Civil Engineers. Bryan Donkin was born at Sandoe, Northumberland, where his father, a surveyor and land agent, was an acquaintance of Smeaton whom he consulted as to how to become an engineer. On Smeaton's advice he was apprenticed to John Hall of Dartford, Kent. Donkin helped to develop paper-making machinery and became interested in the preservation of meat and vegetables in airtight cans. In 1815 his practice expanded into the field of civil engineering, operating from an office in Bermondsey.

Joshua Field was the eldest of the eight young engineers who, led by Henry Robinson Palmer, had founded the Institution of Civil Engineers. On leaving school he had obtained a place at Portsmouth Dockyard through the patronage of General Sir Samuel Bentham and later joined Henry Maudslay, who was making Marc Brunel's block-making machines for the dockyard. In 1822 Field and Henry Maudslay's eldest son Thomas were made partners in the firm which was renamed Maudslay, Son and Field.

James Simpson was a water engineer, the fourth son of Thomas Simpson, engineer of the Chelsea Waterworks whom he succeeded when his father died. James also followed his father as engineer of the Lambeth Water Co.

There was a large attendance at the last meeting of the 1834 session. Guests were paid for by their hosts at the same rate as the members themselves i.e. 9s, and this was supplemented from the Society's general funds. The amounts which fell to the Society were greatly increased on this occasion, running into an adverse balance of £10 19s 0d at the end of the year, which the Treasurer was obliged to advance.

The Society's indebtedness to the Treasurer had increased to £24 by the end of the 1836 session, so the annual subscription was increased to £2 again. By the end of 1838 the Treasurer had been reimbursed and there was a balance in hand of 15s.

Colonel George Landmann, RE, and Joseph Miller became ordinary members in 1836. At the age of 15 Miller was an articled pupil of Boulton and Watt, Birmingham, and in 1817, at the age of 20, he was taken on by William Jessop, jnr, to manage the mechanical engineering department of Butterley Ironworks. In partnership with

James Barnes he set up a factory for the production of marine steam engines in 1822. The partnership was dissolved in 1835 and Miller continued on his own. He was a benefactor of the Institution of Civil Engineers, providing prizes and scholarships for Associate Members and Students.

Also in 1836 two honorary members were elected, Dr Peter Mark Roget, Secretary of the Royal Society, and the Reverend William Whewell of Trinity College, Cambridge. A new list of members was printed.

In 1837 Marc Isambart Brunel was elected. Born to an old French farming family living in Normandy, he attended school in Rouen and then went to sea. After the French Revolution he emigrated to America and worked there as a surveyor before taking American citizenship to become the City Engineer of New York. He came to England in 1799 to design and install his blockmaking machinery at Portsmouth Dockyard. He was a prolific inventor with many patents to his credit, but his main achievement, which occupied nearly 20 years of his life, was the first Thames Tunnel. This was through by 1841 and when it was opened in 1843 he was knighted, taking the title Sir Isambart Brunel.

There were two elections in 1838: John Macneill, one of Telford's former assistants, who had become a railway engineer, as an ordinary member, and Captain Henry Brandreth, RE, an honorary member. Francis Bramah became an honorary member a year later.

The next admissions were in 1841, when Isambard Kingdom Brunel, who had been the resident engineer under his father on the Thames Tunnel, and James Meadows Rendel, the West Country engineer, who had opened a London office in 1838, were both elected.

Overdue subscriptions continued to be a bugbear in a Society with such slender finances. The outstanding debt had risen to £24 again in 1840, excluding £2 owed by Davies Giddy Gilbert, who had died on 24 December 1839, a debt which was by custom written off. Country members were not required to pay an annual subscription, and four members qualified for this relief: James Watt, jnr, of Birmingham; William Jessop, jnr, of Butterley, Derbyshire, and based in Edinburgh; Robert Stevenson; and James Jardine.

The resolution to found the Society in 1771 provided that it would consist of civil engineers and other members. In the beginning there were seven engineers. Twenty years later there were ten, with seven other members associated with engineering but not engineers by profession. Although reorganised in 1793 to include eight engineers and eight members associated with engineering, six honorary members were added. By 1811 there were eight engineers and four non-engineers, but the Society had grown as the class of "Gentlemen" added 21 to the membership. This imbalance had barely changed after another 20 years, and in 1830 there were ten ordinary members and 23 honorary members. Over the next ten years the number of engineers increased, and by 1840 had reached 15, whereas the number of honorary members had dwindled.

The increase in the number of engineer members reflected, to some extent, the quickening pace of industrial development during the first 40 years of the 19th century. The building of canals, inland navigations and turnpikes had given way to the development of harbours and docks, and the railway age had begun. Wind and water power were overtaken rapidly by steam engines.

These works and schemes of drainage and water supplies represented an ever increasing demand for undertakings of public and private enterprise at home and abroad. Opportunities for engineers were expanding. The Society and the Institution had their several parts to play in this rapid development. The Society attracted the eminent engineers and other important gentlemen, to dine and get to know each other better, but it no longer received the gifts of reports, plans and treatises as it had before. The Institution was the learned society, advancing the acquisition of knowledge in the profession by young and old alike.

Chapter Four

1841–1870

When the 1841 session opened on 27 January notice was given of three resolutions

"1. That it is expedient that the Society do elect annually a President,
  2. That Sir John Rennie be requested to preside as President of this Society for the year 1841,
  3. That the President elect do take the Chair at all meetings of the Society, but that in the case of his absence the Chair to be taken as heretofore by the member who shall last enter the room".

These were discussed and carried unanimously at the next meeting by the 15 members present.

For nearly half a century the Society had been led by the Treasurer, the holder of the only office. He administered the Society, his clerk issued the summonses, kept the accounts and was reimbursed for his expenditure on the Society's behalf. The Treasurer was also the banker, advancing money when needed and holding the balance when there was one (the Society did not have a bank account). The Treasurer was to continue these functions, but the most eminent members were, in future, to play a more active role in the affairs of the Society.

The new President was the second son of John Rennie, Treasurer 1812–21. He was born at Stamford Street, Blackfriars, on 30 August 1794, and after school at Dr Greenlaw's, Isleworth, and Dr Burney's at Greenwich, he entered his father's factory in Holland Street, Blackfriars. He worked under the resident engineer on Waterloo Bridge and assisted in the building of Southwark Bridge. He then spent time abroad, studying engineering works on the Continent. On the death of his father he continued in partnership with his brother, carrying on the constructural side of their engineering work. When in 1831 he completed the building of London Bridge, designed by his father, he received a knighthood. He succeeded his father as engineer to the Admiralty, completing work at Sheerness, Woolwich, Ramsgate and the great breakwater at Plymouth. He worked on the drainage of the Fens and on the construction of harbours in England and Ireland.

William Chadwell Mylne, the Treasurer, who continued in office, took on a dual role in 1842 when, at the opening meeting, he was elected President. Since taking over as Treasurer in 1822 he had completed waterworks in several parts of the country, but his main work was the development of the New River Co. He laid cast iron mains and service pipes to replace Myddelton's old wooden ones and constructed settling reservoirs for the better supply of water to districts of North London. He too was concerned with improvements to the drainage of the Fens.

During 1842 the monthly meetings were well attended, and visitors were welcomed on most occasions. The financial position of the Society was healthy and the annual subscription was reduced to £1. The number of ordinary members continued to grow. John Murray of Sunderland, Jesse Hartley, the Liverpool Docks engineer, Joseph Glynn of Butterley Ironworks and Edward Bury of Wolverton were all elected.

The President for the 1843 session was Bryan Donkin, who by then was one of the eldest members, aged 74 years. In December 1844 he claimed that his advanced age rendered exposure to the night air dangerous, and said no longer would he attend the meetings. Sir Isambart Brunel also sent in his resignation. He had been living in Chilcompton, near Bath, for some time, and although he had returned to London again to a house in Park Street, Mayfair, ill health prevented his attending.

The Reverend William Whewell, Master of Trinity College, Cambridge, was present at the meeting on 14 June 1843, and

Motto proposed by Reverend William Whewell

proposed a new motto for the summons card, which he entered in the Minute Book by his own hand. It was adopted as an addition to the card, which was then re-engraved.

In 1844 the President was George Rennie, John's eldest son. He was educated at Dr Greenlaw's, Isleworth, St Paul's School and the University of Edinburgh, before entering his father's office in 1811. For eight years, 1818–26, he held the appointment of Inspector of Machinery at the Royal Mint. On the death of his father in 1821 he carried on the family engineering practice in partnership with his brother, undertaking the construction of Grosvenor Bridge at Chester and railway projects in England and in Belgium. He concentrated on the manufacturing side of the family business; he invented the first biscuit making machine; produced machinery for the Admiralty, corn and chocolate mills for the victualling yards at Deptford and Plymouth, and engines for naval ships. He was one of the pioneers of screw propulsion.

William Cubitt was elected President for 1845. He was born at Dilham, Norfolk, and after his apprenticeship to a cabinet maker, worked for an agricultural machinery maker until 1812 when he joined Messrs Ransomes & Co., Ipswich, and became their Chief Engineer. His interest was in windmills, and he patented a self-adjusting sail. In 1818 he invented the human treadmill, and it was adopted in all the principal gaols of the country. Having established his own engineering practice in 1821, he moved to London in 1826 and was involved in several railway projects, including the Croydon Atmospheric Railway and the South Eastern Railway.

During Cubitt's year of office the ties between the Society and the Institution of Civil Engineers, of which he was a Vice President, were strengthened.

Seven new ordinary members were elected in March, six of whom were senior members of the Institution. They were Robert Stephenson, Joseph Locke, William Gravatt, George Lowe, Charles Vignoles and Charles Manby. The seventh was Robert William Mylne, the Treasurer's son. At the April meeting all the documents, papers, plans, books, etc. which the Society had received over the years were presented to the Institution. They were delivered into the hands of Charles Manby, the Secretary of the Institution, at the close of the meeting.

When Dr Roget became President in 1846 he was the first honorary member to be elected to that office. Peter Mark Roget was a physician, but he is best known for the *Thesaurus of English Words and Phrases* that bears his name. He started to compile this in 1805 for his own use when lecturing, and it was first published in 1852.

The next session opened on 27 January 1847; William Cubitt proposed Robert Stephenson for President, and he was duly elected. Cubitt also proposed George Stephenson for membership, seconded by Joseph Glynn, and he was elected at the meeting on 26 May. George died in August of the following year, not having attended any meetings.

Robert was George's only son. When he left Dr Bruce's Academy in Newcastle-upon-Tyne he was apprenticed to Nicholas Wood, a colliery viewer. He assisted his father in the survey of the Stockton and Darlington line and then spent six months at Edinburgh University. In 1823 the firm of Robert Stephenson & Co. was established for the manufacture of machinery, and he was appointed as the managing partner. He went to Colombia in 1824 and for three years superintended the gold and silver mines of the Colombian Mining Association. He arrived back in Liverpool in December 1827, when George's work on the Liverpool and Manchester Railway was nearing completion. The Rainhill locomotive trials in 1829 were part of the Stephensons' active promotion of the locomotive as the best mode of railway traction, against the protagonists of horses or fixed winding engines. Having won the trial with his *Rocket*, Robert turned to railway construction from 1829 onwards. He entered Parliament in 1847 as the member for Whitby, and continued to represent it for the rest of his life.

A considerable change in the membership of the Society had taken place over a comparatively short time. Between 1830 and 1840 the number of engineers had increased from 10 to 15 and between 1840 and 1845, from 15 to 31, whereas the number of honorary members had dwindled from 23 in 1830, to eight. This preponderance of engineers was consistent with the original aim of the Society, and it reflected the growth and importance of the profession in the early Victorian era. The list of members which was printed in 1847 contained the names of 32 ordinary members and eight honorary members.

Joshua Field was elected President of the Society in January 1848, and in the same month he became the President of the Institution of Civil Engineers of which he was one of the founders. Colonel Colby, the Director of the Ordnance Survey, who had moved to Southampton, asked to be transferred to the "country list": this was approved and his arrears of subscriptions were cancelled.

The Reverend William Whewell sent a letter to explain that he was unable to attend the meetings in general, but he wished to retain his name on the lists of the Society as a "country member" and this was readily agreed.

John Taylor, who was the President in 1849, had been an honorary member for more than 25 years; he was the manager of mines in the West Country and in 1812 founded a chemical factory in Essex. He was the mineral agent of the Duke of Devonshire and of the Commissioners of Greenwich Hospital, also one of the founders of University College, London. Philip, his younger brother, who was an engineer, became an ordinary member in 1824, but resigned on moving to France two years later.

In January 1849 Charles Hampden Turner, a city merchant, was elected an honorary member, and William Cotton joined in May. At the age of 15, Cotton, had entered the counting-house of Charles Turner and six years later, in 1807, became a partner and later managing director of Huddart & Co., Limehouse, a firm founded to develop Captain Joseph Huddart's inventions for the manufacture of cordage. He was elected a director of the Bank of England in 1821 and served as Governor for three years.

The President in 1850 was James Simpson, the Chelsea and Lambeth water engineer. This was at a time when public attention was being focussed on the need for proper sewerage and drainage of towns and better supplies of water of high quality. The Cornish pumping engines which were being used at this time had reached the limit of their development, and Simpson turned to developing the compound rotative beam engine for pumping. These he started manufacturing at Pimlico. His projects included a water supply to Windsor Castle in the 1820s and water supply schemes in Newcastle, Bristol, Liverpool and many smaller towns during the 1830s and 40s. But his achievements were not confined to water supplies; he built the long pier at Southend and the docks at West Hartlepool.

In response to some criticism, a change was made in the rules, to ensure that members had adequate advance warning of elections to membership. Prior notice was to be given, in future, of the date of election and the names of the candidates. The annual subscription, which had been raised to £2 in 1845, was increased to £3, and each member's contribution to the dinner bill which amounted to less than half of the cost of dinner, was increased from 9s to 10s, the balance being met from the general funds of the Society, as before.

Thomas Lloyd, a former shipwright apprentice and student at the School of Naval Architecture, who was involved in steam machinery at the dockyards and its introduction to the Royal Navy, was for many years the Chief Engineer at Woolwich Dockyard. He was appointed to the Admiralty in 1847 and promoted to Chief Engineer of the Royal Navy in 1850. Although he had only joined the Society in April 1849, he was elected President on 15 January 1851.

List of Foreigners & Gentlemen who dined at the Freemasons Tavern on the 30th of May by the invitation of the Society

General Poncelet ——— France —
Colonel A. Morin ——— "
Baron C. Dupin ——— "
Baron Seguier ——— "
Mr M. Mathieu ——— "
Mr Payen ——— "
Mr Combes ——— "
Mr Quetelet ——— Belgium
Chevalier Conrad —— Holland
Chevalier de Burg ——— Austria
Professor Colladon —— Switzerland
Professor Corridi ——— Tuscany
M Louis de Cristoforis — Lombardy

Count A? Rosen —— Sweden
Colonel Schwabe —— Russia
Capt. Lisiansky —— "
Mr Hayward —— America
Mr S Webber ——— "
Dr. Smith ——— "
Lord Lovelace ———
Sir John Herschell
Sir David Brewster
Sir Roderick Murchison
Professor Willis
Professor Wheatstone
Mr T B Pentland —

List of Members of the Society of Civil Engineers who dined at the Freemasons Tavern on the 30th of May – 1851 –

Mr W C Mylne
Mr George Rennie
Sir John Rennie
Mr James Walker
Mr James Simpson
Mr Joseph Miller
Mr John Murray
Mr Joseph Glynn
Mr H Wollaston Blake
Mr Robert Stephenson
Mr William Gravatt
Mr Robert W Mylne

Mr Thomas Lloyd
Mr C Hutton Gregory
Mr Peter W Barlow
Mr John Hawkshaw
Capt. Simmons
Mr Charles Babbage
Revd W Whewell
Mr C Hampden Turner
Mr William Cotton
Mr Joseph Baxendale
Mr G B Airy –

The Society's dinner, 30 May 1851

It was to be a memorable year. The depression of the 1830s, the aftermath of the Napoleonic Wars, had gradually been dispelled. "All could look forward to brighter days", said Joshua Field, "when enterprise might again afford employment and reward to talent and industry, calling into action the best energies of the engineering profession".

Hopes were rising in engineering, stemming from the growing public awareness of the need for sanitation, drainage and potable water, expansion of the railways, and development of the docks. Manufacturing was prospering in the Black Country, the Midlands and the North. A "Great Exhibition of the Works of Industry of all Nations", was proposed by the Society of Arts (the abridged name of the Society for the encouragement of Arts, Manufactures and Commerce) and strongly supported by Prince Albert, the Prince Consort. It was proposed to hold it in 1851, and on 3 January 1850 a Royal Commission was appointed to organise it, with Prince Albert as President. William Cubitt was a member of the Commission and he was appointed chairman of the building committee, to which Robert Stephenson and Isambard Brunel were also appointed. Charles Manby was released from his duties as Secretary of the Institution of Civil Engineers to serve the Commission. Due to the heavy work load the tasks imposed upon them, Cubitt withdrew from the Society in January 1851 and Manby did so in March.

The Crystal Palace was completed by March and the Great Exhibition opened on 1 May. The Society played no part in the exhibition as a body, but its members individually were deeply involved. The exhibition attracted celebrated men of science and of the arts, as well as the producers and manufacturers of all nations, and the opportunity was seized by the Society to entertain important visitors to London. A committee was formed to arrange a dinner on 30 May and to issue the invitations. The committee comprised George Rennie, Joseph Glynn, Thomas Lloyd, William Mylne and William Gravatt. Robert W. Mylne acted as Secretary. The dinner was held at the Freemasons Tavern and 50 members and guests attended.

There were eight new members in 1851: Charles Hutton Gregory, Alfred Burges, the partner of James Walker, Peter William Barlow, John Hawkshaw and Alan Stevenson, Robert's eldest son, were elected as ordinary members; and Joseph Baxendale, Captain J. L. A. Simmons, RE, and Professor George Biddell Airy, the Astronomer Royal who had succeeded Pond in 1835, became honorary members.

Alan Stevenson succeeded his father as engineer to the Commissioners of Northern Lighthouses, but became paralysed in 1852 and retired from the Society; David, his younger brother, the engineer of canals and river navigations, was elected in June 1853.

James Walker became the President in 1852. He was born in Falkirk, went to the local school and Glasgow University. He was a pupil of his uncle, Ralph Walker, the engineer who practised in London Docks. James was engaged in the construction of the East and West India Docks. He specialised in maritime works at first, and became the advisor to the Elder Brethren of Trinity House, the Admiralty and the City Corporation of London. Later his practice extended to railways.

On completing his year of office as President of the Society he expressed a wish to retire from it, in view of his declining health, but was persuaded to accept transfer to "country membership" instead. Charles Babbage and Sir John Macneill also tendered letters of resignation but were transferred to the "country list".

The President who took office in 1853 was Charles Blacker Vignoles, the grandson of Dr Charles Hutton. His name is usually associated with railways, but he had as wide a practice and as varied a career as any civil engineer of his generation. When George and John Rennie were called upon to resurvey the Liverpool and Manchester line after the Bill for it had failed in parliament in 1825, Vignoles carried out the survey and was appointed resident engineer for the western section. When University College, London, founded its first chair of civil engineering in 1841, Vignoles was the first Professor. He worked in America and in Russia, where his suspension bridge at Kiev was the largest in the world at the time of its construction.

The next President was Joseph Baxendale, who was born in Lancaster and in 1817 entered the firm of Pickford & Co., becoming the leading partner and then manager for the rest of his life. As head of the largest firm of carriers in the country, Baxendale was in contact with canal, turnpike and railway engineers. He was a friend of George and Robert Stephenson and, as chairman of the South Eastern Railway Co., a friend of William Cubitt, its engineer. He worked with James Rendel and was a director of the East Indian Railway Co. Although only becoming an honorary member in 1851, he was elected President in 1854. This was to be a momentous year for Europe and not least for the engineers.

The third meeting of the 1854 session was held on 29 March, the day after the declaration of war against Russia. The Crimean War had begun. Many members were to become involved. The next meeting, which should have been held on 26 April, was deferred, as that day had been set apart as a "Day of Humiliation". The meeting took place on 3 May, when it was announced that a son and heir had been born to Robert Mylne on 2 April. A resolution was passed "that the Members congratulate Mr R. W. Mylne and his father their respected Treasurer and express their sincere wish that the boy may live and prosper to a good old age and worthily continue the long line of engineers and architects from whom he is descended".

As the war progressed, the demand for machinery, tools and stores of all kinds filled the factories with orders and gave rise to full employment, but public works were restricted to the execution of work in progress, scarcely any new projects being undertaken. Not only the military were directly involved in the war. Isambard Brunel was engaged in the design and construction of a prefabricated hospital at Rankioi; others were building roads in the war zone and a railway from Balaclava to Sebastopol.

But despite the war, meetings of the Society continued to be held and the attendance was much the same as usual. In 1855 Sir John Rennie became the President for a second term. The rules provided that a President would not be eligible for re-election for two years after holding office, and Sir John's first term had been in 1841. Robert Stephenson served as President for the second time in 1856. In 1849 he had succeeded his father as President of the newly formed Institution of Mechanical Engineers in Birmingham where he served for five years, but his active engineering career had virtually ended with the completion of the Royal Border Bridge over the Tweed and his Britannia Bridge over the Menai Straits in 1850.

Meetings followed the traditional pattern, monthly from 30 January to 25 June. Colonel Simmons, who had been engaged on active service, was excused his arrears of annual subscriptions. The balance of funds in the hands of the Treasurer had increased, and in consequence the subscription was reduced to 30s. It was reduced again in 1857 to £1.

The war ended with the signing of the Peace of Paris on 30 March 1856, and hopes were high that it would after a reasonable interval lead to the resumption of works of public and private enterprise. But this was not the case. The monetary crisis which resulted from the heavy cost of the war retarded the resumption of capital projects at home. There were opportunities abroad, however, mainly in the fields of drainage, water supply and railway engineering, which the British engineers were ready to pursue.

The development of India was pioneered by British engineers. The harnessing of the great rivers was the work of the engineers trained at the East India Company's Engineering College, Addiscombe, founded in 1809. The laying of the railways which followed was no less an achievement. In 1857 work was impeded by the outbreak of

Charles Vignoles   *Robert Stephenson*

the Indian Mutiny, but when strife ceased and the Crown took over the government of India from the East India Company in August 1858, the way was clear not only for further development but also for the training of Indian engineers at the government colleges at Roorkee, Bombay and Calcutta.

Members of the Society were engaged in important projects in India, the Colonies and Empire. As the reputation of British engineers flourished and was more widely recognised, they worked in overseas territories worldwide.

That the London based consulting engineers gathered together is probably due less to the need for interaction between them, than to the common desire to be close to government offices and Parliament where they were frequently heavily engaged. The area favoured was Great George Street, Westminster and the two short turnings off it; Storey's Gate to the south and Duke Street, now overbuilt by government offices, to the north. The street directory of 1856–57 reveals that, in addition to the offices of public works contractors like Peto and Betts at No. 9, Great George Street accommodated a number of railway companies and was the stronghold of the civil engineers, of whom the following were, or were to become, members of the Society.

In Great George Street, the list ran as follows: 6, Joseph Cubitt; 16, John Frederic Bateman; 17, John Robinson McClean; 19, Sir William Cubitt; 23, James Walker and Alfred Burges; 24, Robert Stephenson, George Robert Stephenson, George Berkley, George Bidder and Edwin Clark; 25, The Institution of Civil Engineers and Charles Manby; 26, Peter William Barlow; 27, Alfred Giles; 29, James Simpson; 30, Thomas Hawksley and Nathaniel Beardmore; 33, John Hawkshaw and J. Clarke Hawkshaw. William Pole had his office at 3 Storey's Gate, and in Duke Street Joseph Locke was at No. 13; Isambard Brunel at No. 18; and Charles and Hutton Vignoles at No. 21.

James Walker, who had been put on the "country" list in 1853 on grounds of ill health, recovered, returned to London and resumed his practice in January 1857. It was suggested to him that he should pay an annual subscription once more. He agreed and was restored to the ordinary members' list in March 1858. He retired three years later.

The President in 1857 was John Hawkshaw, who was born at Leeds and trained as a mining engineer. He worked for Jesse Hartley as a young assistant, at Liverpool, and then went to Venezuela for a time. On his return he set up his own practice in London. He worked on London's underground railway and on the Manchester and Leeds Railway before joining Isambard Brunel on the Great Western Railway. He was the engineer of the South Dock in London Docks, the Severn Tunnel and the Amsterdam Ship Canal.

The 1857 session ended on a convivial note; in view of the flourishing state of the Society's finances, an extra dinner was held: 17 members and 21 visitors were present at the Ship Hotel, Greenwich on 11 July.

The Society was sufficiently affluent in 1858 to hold another special dinner at the end of the session, and the President, Henry Wollaston Blake presided at the Star and Garter, Richmond, in July. Blake was educated at Eton and Trinity College, Cambridge, where he became a "wrangler". He entered the office of Thompson Hankey, Governor of the Bank of England, who sent him to America for a time. On his return he joined Boulton and Watt (later James Watt & Co.) the makers of machinery, at Birmingham. He was also a director of several railway companies and a partner with Joseph Baxendale in Pickford & Co.

The Treasurer, William Mylne was elected President for a second term of office in 1859, the year when Frederic Bateman and Bryan Donkin, jnr, became ordinary members.

The session ended in June but that year was a tragic one, not only for the members of the Society but for the engineering profession as a whole. Isambard Brunel died in September and Robert Stephenson in October. Their untimely deaths while still in their 50s were no doubt accelerated by their severe mental and physical exertions throughout their pioneering lives. Although in their professional work they were frequently in dispute and in their own practices pursued policies which differed widely, they used to meet on a perfectly friendly footing and discuss engineering points. The Society provided an opportunity for such amicable discussion: that was its primary purpose. Shortly after his death a number of Isambard Brunel's friends founded a company to build his Clifton Suspension Bridge "as a monument to their late friend and colleague". John Hawkshaw was appointed engineer to the company and, with the assistance of William Barlow, the bridge was completed in December 1864.

John Murray was the President in 1860, He had been a pupil of William Mylne, and in 1831 was appointed as engineer to the River Wear Commissioners; on the formation of the Sunderland Dock Co. he became its engineer, eventually starting his consulting engineer's practice in Parliament Street, Westminster.

In February, William Fairbairn of Manchester, and Thomas Page, who had worked on the Thames Tunnel under Marc Brunel and was engaged in the development of the Thames embankment, were elected ordinary members, and George Banks Rennie joined a month later.

At the opening meeting of the 1861 session George Rennie tendered his resignation on grounds of ill health, but was put on the "country" list instead. The meeting then proceeded to the ballot for the President and William Gravatt was elected. He was born at Gravesend, and at the age of 15 his father, Colonel Gravatt, RE, persuaded Bryan Donkin to accept him as a pupil. On leaving Donkin he was placed with Marc Brunel and worked on the Thames Tunnel. When work on the tunnel stopped in 1832 he was appointed engineer to the Calder and Hebble Navigation. He worked under Henry Palmer on the London and Dover line and under Isambard Brunel on the Great Western Railway. The "dumpy" level and staff was one of his inventions, which he described in a paper he read at the Institution of Civil Engineers for which he was awarded a Telford Silver Medal.

It was drawn to the attention of members by John Hawkshaw and John Fowler that 1861 was the 50th anniversary of the election to membership of the Treasurer, William Mylne, and they proposed that the occasion be marked by a celebratory dinner. A small committee of Hawkshaw, Fowler and Sir John Rennie organised this, and the dinner was held at the Freemasons Tavern on 31 July.

1861 —

*Dinner given by the Members of the Smeatonian
Society of Civil Engineers to Mr W.C. Mylne in
honor of his 50th year of Membership —*

List of Members & visitors attending

Mr W. C. Mylne

Mr W. Gravatt

Mr W. Blake

Mr W. Fairbairn

Capt D. Galton RE.

Mr P. Barlow

Mr G. B. Rennie

Mr R W Mylne

Mr J. Simpson

Sir J. Rennie

Mr J. Murray

Mr T Lloyd —

Sir H. O. Fleetwood

Jno S. C. Whitbread

Mr T W. Rammell

Mr J. Simpson Junr

Mr Robt Chambers

Mr D. McGrigor

Mr C Rivington

Mr J. W. Prout

Mr J. M White

Mr C. Greaves

Mr J. Marchant

Dr Spurgin —

Mr Field —

14 Members were unable to attend

5 Country members were also absent

Dinner to W.C. Mylne, 31 July 1861

SMEATONIAN SOCIETY OF CIVIL ENGINEERS.

From the " BUILDER*," August 3rd, 1861.*

"THIS Society, on Wednesday Evening, the 31st instant, gave a Special Dinner at the Freemasons' Hall to their respected Treasurer, Mr. Mylne, on the occasion of his fiftieth year of membership of the Society. About thirty gentlemen, including visitors, sat down to a sumptuous repast, and Mr. Wm. Gravatt, the President of the year, took the Chair.

"After Dinner, the standard toasts of the Society were given. The health of Mr. Mylne was proposed by Sir John Rennie, who first touched upon the history of the Society; saying it was founded, in 1771, by Mr. Smeaton, for the purpose of encouraging civil engineers, and introducing, through social meetings, a friendly intercourse among men of science and the profession at large. Among the early Members of the Society were the names of Watt, Jessop, Whitworth, Brindley, Rennie, Mylne, Huddart, and Chapman; and later, those of Banks, Priestley, Evelyn, Boulton, Hutton, &c. A graceful notice of the merits and urbanity of disposition of the worthy Treasurer was made, and great praise was given for his constant exertions towards maintaining the high position of the Society. Mr. Mylne, in reply, said it was one of the highest gratifications to see his professional brethren joining in so marked a compliment; that the Society had ever been one of great interest to him; and he had always endeavoured to maintain its character, and draw together opposing parties. After a long life, he was now proud to find such warm feelings of regard and respect.

"Mr. Fairbairn proposed 'The Visitors' in a brief speech, which was replied to by Mr. Robert Chambers. After alluding to the peculiar gratification that he felt in being favoured with the opportunity of paying a tribute of regard to his friend, he could not refrain, he said, from alluding to the long line of engineers and architects that the Scottish race of Mylne had produced. He could speak with certainty to nine consecutive generations, with every reason to believe there were three previous to them; and he was sure it must be a source of deep gratification to Mr Mylne to see that the hereditary profession was still continued by his son, the Vice-President of the evening. He thanked them all in the name of the visitors.

"The party broke up at a late hour."

Extract from the Builder, 3 August 1861

Mylne's name was added to the "country list", thus exempting him from further subscriptions.

A second Great Exhibition took place at South Kensington in the summer of 1862. It was not on the same scale as that of 1851; nevertheless members were deeply involved. Several members of the Society were appointed to the central committee, representing various classes of exhibits, e.g. railway plant, locomotives and carriages; manufacturing machinery and tools; machinery in general; and civil engineering, architectural and building equipment. Those appointed included John Robinson McClean, a former pupil and assistant of James Walker; Joseph Cubitt, Sir William's only son; George Hemans, and Captain Douglas Galton.

As in 1851 a dinner was arranged by the Society for the entertainment of distinguished foreign visitors connected with science and engineering. It was organised by a committee chaired by the President, Charles Hutton Gregory. Gregory was the son of Dr Olinthus Gregory, Professor of Mathematics at the RMA, Woolwich. Much of his work was executed abroad: he was the consulting engineer to the Crown Agents for the Colonies and to colonial governments, mainly in the construction of railways. The other members of the dinner committee were Gravatt, Lloyd, Vignoles, Bateman and the Treasurer, William Mylne. The dinner was held on 12 June at the Ship Hotel, Greenwich, when 50 sat down at table.

Colonel J. L. A. Simmons, CB, RE, was elected President in 1863. From Elizabeth College, Guernsey and RMA, Woolwich, he was commissioned in 1837, and soon became involved with railways: as an inspector, as Secretary to the Railway Commission and Secretary to the Railway Division, Board of Trade. He saw active service in the Russo-Turkish War and the Crimea. After two years as Consul General in Warsaw he returned to Aldershot in 1860 and resumed his attendance at the Society's meetings. He chaired the meeting on 21 January, when two resolutions were proposed by Charles Gregory.

"1. That notice shall be sent to every Member of the Society, of the name of every gentleman proposed as a Member, fourteen days previous to the meeting at which it is proposed that his elections shall take place.
2. That all Members shall be elected by ballot and that three black balls shall exclude any person being Member of the Society".

Discussion of the resolutions was due to take place on 25 February, but the first resolution was withdrawn as the matter was said to be covered by the somewhat similar resolution passed on 23 January 1850; the second resolution, when put to the vote, was negatived.

Nathaniel Beardmore was elected an ordinary member. He was a former pupil of James Rendel and became his partner, running the Plymouth office when Rendel moved to London. His partnership with Rendel ended in 1848 and he set up his own practice in Great George Street. Two honorary members were elected, Lieut. Col. W. F. D. Jervois, RE, and Major General F. R. Chesney, RA.

As had happened in earlier years, a special dinner was planned at the end of the 1863 session, and out of consideration for the Treasurer and as a tribute to him, it was held as close to his residence at Great Amwell, Herts., as could conveniently be arranged. It took place at Broxbourne, and those who attended travelled by special train. Mylne died on Christmas Day, only five months later. He had been a member for 52 years and had served for 41 years as Treasurer. The great respect in which the members held him, and their appreciation of the valuable services rendered by him, were recorded in the Minutes of the meeting of 17 February 1864, and a copy of the Minute, written on vellum, was sent to his widow.

Robert William Mylne was elected Treasurer in succession to his father. He was born on 14 June 1817, and practised as an architect, engineer and geologist. After working on the harbour at Sunderland, he travelled abroad in Italy and Sicily, returning in 1842 to assist his father. He held the post of engineer to the Limerick Water Co. for some time and was mainly engaged in water supply and drainage schemes.

In 1864 there were two new ordinary members, whose firms eventually amalgamated: Joseph Whitworth, founder of the tool making firm of Joseph Whitworth and Co., Manchester, and Sir William Armstrong, whose factory at Elswick made hydraulic machinery, guns and ammunition and later undertook naval shipbuilding.

William Lindley was the President in 1864. He was educated partly in Germany, in which country he was later to make his name. In 1827 he became a pupil of Francis Giles and was chiefly engaged in railway work. In 1838 he was appointed engineer to the Hamburg Bergedorf Railway and worked in Hamburg for the next 20 years. His work included Hamburg's sewage and waterworks, land drainage and reclamation. He left Hamburg in 1860 and returned to London. After his year of office, early in 1865, he was appointed consulting engineer to the city of Frankfurt and returned to Germany.

Peter William Barlow succeeded Lindley as President in February 1865. He was the eldest son of Peter Barlow, Professor at the RMA, Woolwich, and in 1826 he became a pupil of Henry Palmer, who was at that time an assistant engineer to Thomas Telford. Under Palmer,

LIST OF THE MEMBERS

OF THE

SMEATONIAN SOCIETY OF CIVIL ENGINEERS.

FOUNDED 1771.

June, 1845.	June, 1882.
Date of Election.	*Date of Election.*
1811 WILLIAM C. MYLNE, F.R.S., *Treasurer.*	1843 H. WOLLASTON BLAKE, M.A., F.R.S.
1822 GEORGE RENNIE, F.R.S.	1844 WILLIAM LINDLEY.
„ SIR JOHN RENNIE, F.R.S.	1845 ROBERT W. MYLNE, F.R.S.
1824 JAMES WALKER, F.R.S.	1851 C. HUTTON GREGORY, C.M.G.
1825 WILLIAM JESSOP.	„ DAVID STEVENSON, F.R.S., E.
1827 JAMES JARDINE, F.R.S., E.	„ SIR JOHN HAWKSHAW, F.R.S.
„ ROBERT STEVENSON, F.R.S., E.	1854 JOHN FOWLER.
1831 WILLIAM CUBITT, F.R.S., *President.*	1857 JAMES LESLIE, F.R.S., E.
1832 WM. TIERNEY CLARKE, F.R.S.	„ ALFRED GILES.
10 1835 JOSHUA FIELD, F.R.S	10 1859 JOHN FREDERICK BATEMAN, F.R.S.
„ JAMES SIMPSON	„ BRYAN DONKIN.
1836 COLONEL LANDMANN.	1860 GEORGE BANKS RENNIE.
„ JOSEPH MILLER, F.R.S.	1864 SIR JOS. WHITWORTH, BART., D.C.L., LL.D., F.R.S.
1838 MAJOR BRANDRETH, R.E., F.R.S.	„ SIR WM. G. ARMSTRONG, C.B., M.A., D.C.L., F.R.S.
„ SIR JOHN MACNEIL, F.R.S.	1865 WILLIAM HENRY BARLOW, F.R.S.
1841 ISAMBARD K. BRUNEL, F.R.S.	„ THOMAS E. HARRISON.
„ JAMES M. RENDEL, F.R.S.	1867 SIR JOSEPH W. BAZALGETTE, C.B.
1842 JOHN MURRAY.	„ JAMES BRUNLEES, F.R.S., E.
„ JOSEPH GLYNN, F.R.S.	„ JAMES ABERNETHY.
20 „ JESSE HARTLEY.	20 1869 JOSEPH QUICK.
„ EDWARD BURY, F.R.S.	„ C. WILLIAM SIEMENS, D.C.L., LL.D., F.R.S.
1843 H. WOLLASTON BLAKE, M.A., F.R.S.	„ SIR FREDERICK J. BRAMWELL, F.R.S.
1844 JOSEPH CUBITT.	1870 GEORGE B. BRUCE.
„ WILLIAM LINDLEY.	„ JOSEPH MITCHELL, F.R.S., E.
1845 JOSEPH LOCKE, F.R.S.	„ ALEXr. MEADOWS RENDEL
„ ROBERT STEPHENSON.	1872 EDWARD WOODS.
„ WILLIAM GRAVATT, F.R.S	„ THOMAS HAWKESLEY, F.R.S.
„ GEORGE LOWE, F.R.S.	1875 WILLIAM POLE, Dr. MUS., F.R.S.
„ CHARLES MANBY.	1876 CHARLES GREAVES.
„ CHARLES VIGNOLES.	„ J. CLARKE HAWKSHAW.
31 „ ROBERT W. MYLNE.	1878 RICHARD B. GRANTHAM.
	„ HUTTON VIGNOLES.
	1879 J. WOLFE BARRY.
	„ FRANCIS STEVENSON.
	35 1882 JAMES N. DOUGLASS.

HONORARY MEMBERS.	HONORARY MEMBERS.
1810 GEORGE DOLLOND, F.R.S.	1851 GENERAL SIR J. L. A. SIMMONS, R.E., G.C.B.
1822 CHARLES BABBAGE, M.A., F.R.S.	1858 CAPTn. DOUGLAS GALTON, C.B., F.R.S.
„ MAJOR-GENERAL COLBY, R.E., F.R.S.	1865 JOHN PERCY, M.D., F.R.S.
„ JAMES WATT, F.R.S.	1868 HIS GRACE THE DUKE OF SUTHERLAND K.G.
1823 JOHN TAYLOR, F.R.S.	1869 WARINGTON W. SMYTH, M.A., F.R.S.
„ ADMIRAL BEAUFORT, F.R.S.	1874 CLIFFORD WIGRAM.
1836 Dr. P. M. ROGET, M.D., F.R.S.	1877 FREDERICK A. ABEL, C.B., F.R.S.
39 „ Rev. W. WHEWELL, B.D., F.R.S.	1878 COLONEL CROSSMAN, R.E., C.M.G.
	44 „ MAJOR-GEN. YOUNGHUSBAND, R.A., C.B., F.R.S.

List of members, 1845 and 1882

Barlow worked on the Liverpool and Birmingham Canal and then on the new London Docks. He surveyed the route of the London and Dover Railway and in 1836 was appointed resident engineer under William Cubitt. He studied the problem of stiffening the decks of suspension bridges and reported on the bridges over Niagara. He designed the suspension bridges at Lambeth and Kew.

In June 1865 a change in the rules was proposed by the new Treasurer. In place of the existing rule which specified an annual subscription of £2 (and therefore had to be amended from time to time) which had to be collected from all the members except those residing out of London, he proposed "that such annual contribution as shall be determined upon for the current year, at the first meeting of each session, shall be collected from all the members except such as may, by vote of the members, be exempted for special reasons".

This change approved on 31 January 1866, not only avoided frequent amendments to the rule, but brought to an end the practice of adding to the list of "country" members the names of those who, due to ill health or for other reasons, it was desired to exempt from subscriptions, whether they resided out of London or not.

The new rule was exercised forthwith in favour of George Rennie, William Cotton and Charles Babbage. The deaths of George Rennie, William Cotton and also William Gravatt were recorded a year later. George Rennie was the longest serving member of the Society, his membership dating from 1822, the first meeting after the death of his father. He was always very proud of the fact that his birth was recorded in the Minutes of the Society to which his father and he devoted so much active support. He died on 30 March 1866, from the effects of an accident he had suffered the year before. Cotton, who died on 1 December, was a city businessman and philanthropist who did much charity work in the East End of London, especially for children. Gravatt died on 30 May in tragic circumstances. He was accidentally poisoned by a dose of morphine given him inadvertently by his nurse.

Charles Vignoles was elected for a second term as President in 1866. Among the members elected were William Henry Barlow, Peter Barlow's younger brother who was an eminent structural and railway engineer; John Coode, renowned for his maritime works worldwide; Thomas Harrison, an associate of Robert Stephenson, who was responsible for much railway and dock construction in NE England; and George Fosbery Lyster, Engineer-in-Chief of the Mersey Docks and Harbour Board and an ex-pupil of James Rendel. There were two honorary members, the Earl of Caithness and Dr John Percy, MD.

The next President was Alfred Giles, the son of Francis, who was educated at Charterhouse, entered his father's office and worked on the London-Brighton and London-Southampton railway surveys. In 1838 he became assistant to his father, the engineer to the Southampton Docks Co. and succeeded to that office on his father's death in 1847.

Membership continued to expand. In 1867 three new ordinary members were elected in January; Joseph William Bazalgette, James Brunlees and Captain E. Bellfield, RE, and in April James Abernethy was elected and Sir Daniel Gooch, MP, became an honorary member.

John Fowler was one of the members, with Charles Gregory and George Hemans, appointed to the Commission organising the 1867 Universal Exposition in Paris to advise in the various classes of engineering involved. Fowler was elected President in 1868. He was born at Sheffield and at the age of 17 became a pupil of John Towlerton Leather of the Sheffield Waterworks Co. After his pupillage he was employed by J. U. Rastrick and worked for two years on the London and Brighton Railway, then rejoining Leather. He was the resident engineer on the Stockton and Hartlepool line, and worked on railways in Scotland under Sir John Macneill and in the Sheffield area, in Wales, Ireland and India. In 1853, when the first Act was passed, he undertook the construction of the Metropolitan and District Underground railways, against much opposition and scepticism. His health suffered and at the end of the 1868 session he went to Egypt to recuperate.

During the year the Duke of Sutherland was elected an honorary member and in the following year among the new ordinary members were Charles William Siemens, the metallurgist and electrical engineer, Frederick Joseph Bramwell, the mechanical engineer and Warrington Wilkinson Smyth who became an honorary member. John Penn was the President in 1869. His father, of the same name, had started as a millwright at Bridgewater and moved to Greenwich, where he founded the firm making machinery for flour mills. He made the first human treadmill designed by William Cubitt, in 1817. John Penn, the son, was apprenticed to his father and became a partner in the firm John Penn & Sons. In 1825 they began making marine engines.

The meeting of the Society arranged for 28 April was cancelled when it was found to coincide with the Annual Dinner of the Institution of Civil Engineers. Many members of the Society were members of the Institution and some had been Presidents of both, but only Robert Stephenson and Joshua Field held both offices simultaneously. The 1869 session formally closed on 23 June, but an extra dinner was planned, the arrangements being left in the hands of the Treasurer. It took a novel form. The President, John Penn, placed his steam yacht at the disposal of the Society. The members and their guests embarked at Westminster in the early afternoon of 13 July and proceeded down the river, to call first at the President's factory at Deptford and then at Siemens Telegraph Cable Works at Charlton, and the gun and ammunition factories at the Royal Arsenal, Woolwich. The party disembarked for dinner at the Trafalgar Hotel, Greenwich, which was attended by 43 members and guests.

SMEATONIAN SOCIETY OF CIVIL ENGINEERS.— This Society made an Excursion down the River, and afterwards had an Entertainment at Greenwich, on Tuesday, the 13th instant. The Party started from Westminster in Mr. Penn's Steam Yacht, and visited, under special arrangements, his Engine Manufactory at Deptford; also Messrs. Siemens' Telegraph Cable Works at Charlton; and the Gun and Ammunition Factories at the Royal Arsenal, Woolwich. The inspection and the explanations given were of the greatest interest, and afforded much information and pleasure to the Company. At the Dinner there were nearly fifty gentlemen; the Chair was taken by Mr. Penn, the President for the year; and among those present were Lord Lawrence, Sayad Ahmed Khan and his two sons, Lord Alfred Churchill, Thaisz Elek, of Pesth, Baron Jochmus, Hon. J. R. Howard, Messrs. Hawkshaw, Vignoles, Whitworth, Lindley, Hemans, J. R. McClean, M.P, R. Arkwright, M.P., Dr. Percy, Major-Generals Sir A. Waugh and Sir J. A. L. Simmons, Colonels Boxer, Campbell and Murray, Captains Galton and Routh, Aldermen J. S. Gibbons and Sir Sydney Waterlow, &c., &c. The Society dates from 1771, when Smeaton instituted a gathering of Professional Engineers and Men of Science for friendly intercourse and discussion. The usual ancient toasts of the Society were given in the evening, and to that of the Memory of their departed Brethren special notice was made of the name of James Watt by Mr. T. Webster, Q C., being the centenary of his first patent for a Method of lessening the Consumption of Steam and Fuel in Fire Engines, on the 5th January, 1769. For the visitors, Lord A. Churchill and Mr. Reed of the Admiralty replied, together with Lord Lawrence, and with a dignified and interesting speech from his friend the Judge Sayad Ahmed. Thanks were accorded to the President, and to Mr. Mylne, the Treasurer, for the arrangements of the day, and several of the party returned to town in the evening by the steam yacht.

Extract from the Daily News, 21 July 1869

Lieutenant Colonel William Francis Drummond Jervois, RE, was elected President for the 1870 session. Born at Cowes, Isle of Wight, and educated at the Royal Military Academy, Gosport, he was commissioned in the Royal Engineers after attending RMA, Woolwich. He saw active service abroad; against the Boers in 1842 and in the Kaffir War of 1846–47. He became an expert on fortifications, constructing those on Alderney, at Portsmouth and Plymouth and on the Thames and Medway. He served at the War Office from 1856 to 1875 as a specialist on fortifications and attended Society meetings regularly.

Among the new ordinary members elected were George Barclay Bruce, a former pupil of Robert Stephenson; Joseph Mitchell, an ex-pupil of Telford; and Alexander Meadows Rendel, the son of James. Major General John Henry Lefroy, RA, became an honorary member. The amendment to the rules proposed by Charles Gregory in 1863, namely that "three black balls" be substituted for "one black ball" to exclude a candidate from membership under Rule VI had been negatived, but General Simmons raised the matter again at the opening meeting in 1870 and this time it was carried, 14 members voting in favour out of 24 members present.

Chapter Five

1871–1900

The 1871 session started on 25 January but no more than five members were present and although a quorum the election of a President was postponed. On 22 February only seven members and two visitors turned up, and the election was again deferred. On 29 March, John Frederic Bateman was elected. He had been apprenticed to a mining engineer, but at the age of 23 years he set up his own practice as a land surveyor and civil engineer. He worked with William Fairbairn, whose son-in-law he became. His reputation grew and he was acknowledged as one of the leading water engineers of his time, especially as a dam builder.

It was the centenary year of the Society, and 29 March was the anniversary of the first ordinary meeting which had followed the inaugural meeting of the Society in March 1771. A celebratory dinner was held at the usual place, the Freemasons Tavern, and 22 members and eleven visitors were present. The traditional toasts and sentiment were honoured.

Following the dinner a committee was appointed to consider the traditional toasts and sentiment, with a view to recommending any alterations or additions which might be made in the light of the advances in engineering which had taken place over the years. The committee comprised the President, Frederic Bateman; the Treasurer, Robert Mylne; Dr Percy; George Hemans and John Murray, with power to add to their number if they wished. Gregory suggested adding the names of more recent distinguished engineers to the toast "to the memory of our departed brothers", but the committee recommended that no changes be made.

As the session drew to a close, an extra dinner was proposed to honour the 50th anniversary of the membership of Sir John Rennie. John Penn once again placed his steam yacht at the disposal of the members, and at 12.30pm on 23 July the party left Westminster Bridge and proceeded to the works of the Permanent Construction Telegraph Company, then on to the Crossness Pumping Station at

The Centenary Dinner, 29 March 1871

the southern outfall of the South London drainage system, where four beam engines, built by James Watt & Son, discharged the effluent onto the high tide of the lower Thames. After a visit to the gun factory at Woolwich, the party landed at Greenwich for dinner at the Trafalgar Hotel. Sir John was indisposed and could not attend, but after the Lord Mayor of London had proposed his health, the Treasurer read a letter from Sir John expressing his thanks for the honour the Society had accorded him.

Bryan Donkin, who was elected President in 1872, was the fifth son of Bryan Donkin, FRS, the civil engineer and constructor of machinery who had founded the firm of Bryan Donkin & Co. at Bermondsey in 1803 and had been President of the Society in 1843. At his death in 1855 his surviving sons became partners (John, his eldest son, had died the year before). Bryan was educated in England and in France, before entering the Bermondsey Works, eventually becoming the senior partner.

The President in 1873 was George Banks Rennie, the elder son of George. He entered the Navy as a midshipman in 1844, but after a time he left to join the family firm of J. & G. Rennie. His main concern was the building of marine engines and he built the first iron floating dock, which had been ordered by the Spanish Government.

Attendance at the monthly meetings was declining. Ten years before, when the membership was 48, attendance averaged 10, but for the last two years, although the membership had increased to 53, attendance had declined to an average of eight. A special meeting was called in January 1874 to consider how best to reverse this trend. Discussion at the meeting led to no special recommendations but the question was left open for further discussion at the next ordinary meeting: however, no conclusions were reached then.

Another exhibition was planned for 1874, "The London International Exhibition", under the auspices of the Royal Commission for the Exhibition of 1851. As in 1851 and 1862 members of the Society played their individual parts on the general committee, representing their fields of experience. Thomas Harrison, Frederic Bateman and Sir John Coode represented civil engineering, architectural and building contrivances and tests; Frederick Bramwell, Sir Joseph Whitworth and Edward Woods were the representatives of mechanical engineering and Sir William Armstrong, William Siemens and George Robert Stephenson, the son of George's younger brother Robert, covered engineering manufacture.

The Treasurer reported that in the early part of 1873 Sir John Rennie had asked him for the records of the Society with the intention of writing the history of its first 100 years and he had complied with his request. After several meetings between Sir John and the Treasurer, the history was completed and forwarded to the Society through the President in October 1873. It was the Treasurer's view, however, that the whole manuscript needed very material alteration before publication and he suggested to Sir John that it be put before the Society at its next meeting, when he thought it probable that a committee would be set up to revise it. This suggestion was not acceptable to Sir John. In a letter dated 19 January 1874 he asked for the return of his manuscript and it was sent back to him.

Sir John died at his home at Bengeo, Herts., on 3 September 1874. The Treasurer reported the death of Sir John at the meeting in the following January and also the death of Sir William Fairbairn, the pioneer of the use of wrought iron, whose testing of the strength of materials had helped Robert Stephenson with his Britannia and Conway bridges.

The President in 1874 was Dr John Percy, MD, who graduated in medicine at Edinburgh University in 1838 but did not go into medical practice. His interest lay in metallurgy, and he became a lecturer in the newly founded Metropolitan School of Science which in 1851 became the Royal College of Science. In 1864 he was appointed lecturer in metallurgy at the RMA, Woolwich.

The Society had been meeting regularly at the Freemasons Tavern for upwards of 50 years, and when the session ended on 24 June, a vote of thanks was passed to the proprietors, expressing the members' "high appreciation of the present management and approval of the character and of the dinners served by Mr Francatelli".

At the meeting on 20 January 1875, William Henry Barlow was elected President. After three years of practical training, first in Woolwich Dockyard and then in London Docks under Palmer, he joined Maudslay, Son and Field and was sent to Turkey, where he worked for the next six years. On his return in 1838 he was assistant engineer on the Manchester and Birmingham line and eventually became the Engineer-in-Chief of the Midland Railway. In this capacity he helped Joseph Paxton to prepare his proposals for the Crystal Palace. On leaving the railway company he practised as a consultant at 19 Great George Street, and from 1866 onwards at 2 Old Palace Yard.

Robert Joseph Rawlinson and William Pole were elected ordinary members in April. Rawlinson was a pupil of Jesse Hartley at Liverpool Docks and then worked for Robert Stephenson on the London and Birmingham Railway until in 1840 he joined Liverpool Corporation and was responsible for its water supplies and drainage.

After the Public Health Act 1848 he became one of the statutory engineering inspectors. When the Local Government Board (predecessor of the Ministry of Health) was established in 1871 Rawlinson was appointed its Chief Engineering Inspector.

During the Crimean War he had been sent by the government as head of a sanitary commission to remedy the appalling conditions under which the Army was operating. He was struck and wounded by a cannon ball fired by the Russians, which he brought back as a trophy and gave to the Institution of Civil Engineers.

William Pole had surveyed railways in India before becoming the first Professor of Engineering at Elphinstone College, Bombay, in 1844. He returned to England in 1847 and practised as a consulting engineer until he succeeded Vignoles as Professor of Civil Engineering at University College, London, in 1859. He was a doctor of music and wrote authoritatively on his three main topics—engineering, music and whist.

Sir Joseph Bazalgette was elected President in 1876. He had become the Chief Engineer of the Metropolitan Board of Works in 1855 and in the course of the next 20 years was responsible for the main drainage of London. In 1862 the Board was empowered to reconstruct the Thames embankments; bridges were built, and this work occupied Sir Joseph until the Board was replaced by the London County Council in 1889, when he retired.

Two new members were elected in March; they were Charles Greaves and John Clark Hawkshaw. Greaves, a grandson of Robert Mylne and assistant to James Rendel, had been the resident engineer at Acramans Bristol Ironworks, for the construction of Rendel's floating bridges. John Clark Hawkshaw was a partner in the firm founded by his father.

Once again a special dinner was arranged to mark the end of the session, and this time it was combined with a visit to the Royal Dockyard at Chatham. The dinner was held at Greenwich on 5 July and was attended by twelve members and nine visitors. For the next three years the sessions followed a regular pattern. Six meetings each year at the Freemasons Tavern, held between January and June, were followed each year by a special dinner in July held at the Trafalgar Hotel, Greenwich. In 1879, when William Siemens was President, it was preceded by another visit to Chatham Dockyard.

James Abernethy, the President in 1877, was a docks and harbour engineer. He was born in Aberdeen and educated in Scotland but went to London to work under his father, who was the resident engineer in London Docks under Palmer. He later worked on Goole Docks under George Leather, and in 1840 was appointed resident engineer of Aberdeen Harbour, eventually becoming Chief Engineer. In 1854 he opened his own practice in Parliament Street, Westminster. James Brunlees, the next President, was born at Kelso and educated there and at Edinburgh University. After surveying on the Duke of Roxburgh's estate, he worked on several railway schemes; on the Caledonian line and as assistant to John Hawkshaw on the Lancashire and Yorkshire Railway. He was involved with railways in Northern Ireland and in Brazil, where the resident engineer was Douglas Fox.

Charles William Siemens, the President in 1879, was born in Hanover. He was baptised Carl Wilhelm, but having a brother called Carl, was always known as Wilhelm, and changed to William after 1859 when he became a naturalised British subject. With his eldest brother Werner he invented and brought to England an electroplating process. He was an inventor, but after failing to market some of his ideas he joined Fox and Henderson, iron founders of Birmingham, and jointly success followed. With another brother, Frederick, he developed a regenerative furnace, which led to the Siemens Martin process for making steel. In 1847 Werner founded the Berlin firm of Siemens and Halske, and William was its London agent. They developed the electric telegraph and produced insulated cables, including submarine cables and electrical machinery. Under the name Siemens Bros they opened a factory at Charlton, Kent.

In the year 1880 there was confusion. At the meeting on 28 January when only six members and three visitors were present, Frederick Joseph Bramwell was proposed and duly elected President, but he was absent from the meeting and didn't attend any meetings during the session. No explanation is given in the Minutes of the Society but in later years, when the lists of Presidents were printed and published, the year 1880 is marked "not accepted".

Warrington Wilkinson Smyth, geologist and mineralogist, was the President in 1881. His education at Westminster and Bedford schools and Trinity College, Cambridge, was followed by four years travelling abroad. On his return he applied himself to the geological survey of the British Isles, and when the School of Mines was founded in 1851 he lectured there on mining and mineralogy. His wife was a grand-daughter of Dr Nevil Maskelyne, the Astronomer Royal, a former member of the Society. At the end of the 1881 session another special dinner was held, this time at Broxbourne, Herts., not far from the home of Robert Mylne, the Treasurer.

The next President was George Barclay Bruce, who was born at Newcastle-upon-Tyne, the younger son of Dr Bruce, founder of the Percy St. Academy where Robert Stephenson was once a pupil.

William Siemens   *Sir Benjamin Baker*

George served a five year apprenticeship in the locomotive works of R. Stephenson & Co., and after two years' experience on railway construction, he was appointed by Robert Stephenson and Thomas Harrison as resident engineer on the Royal Border Bridge, the North Eastern Railway bridge across the Tweed. Afterwards he worked on railways in India, until in 1856 ill health compelled him to return home. He established his consulting engineering practice in Westminster.

In May, James Nicholas Douglass was proposed for membership and after his election in June the members expressed their great pleasure that the engineer of the new Eddystone Lighthouse had joined the Society which was so closely associated with the engineer of the old one, Smeaton. Smeaton's lighthouse had not been destroyed, but the rock it stood upon had begun to split and so the lighthouse was removed, the upper part being re-erected on Plymouth Hoe.

At the concluding meeting of the session Robert William Mylne resigned the office of Treasurer which he had held for more than 18 years. He was thanked for his long and conscientious service to the Society and assured that he carried with him in retirement the good wishes of all the members. George Banks Rennie was proposed for the office of Treasurer and was elected, having expressed his readiness to take over the task. It was then resolved that a "compendious" history of the Society be compiled containing a list of members "from its earliest commencement until the present day". Mylne and Rennie were asked to compile it and to arrange for a facsimile of the early Minute Book of the Society to be produced.

The 1883 session opened with George Bruce, the retiring President, in the chair. There was one nomination for President, Robert W. Mylne the ex-Treasurer, but he declined, and Sir Frederick Bramwell was nominated and elected. He had been elected in 1880 but had not accepted office then. He was present and, on being elected this time, he took the chair. Bramwell was born in London. His elder brother George, Lord Bramwell, attained eminence at the bar and on the bench. After going to school at Enfield, Frederick was apprenticed to John Hague, a mechanical engineer. He assisted Hague with his atmospheric railway experiments, rope haulage tramways and steam driven road carriages. In 1853 Bramwell set up his own practice, but soon turned to consultancy on legal problems of construction. In 1860 he took an office at 35A Great George Street and practised as an expert witness, assessor or technical advocate in the committee rooms of Parliament, in the courts and as an arbitrator. He became an authority on municipal and water engineering cases.

In a new Minute Book the newly appointed Treasurer, George Banks Rennie, recorded the customary toasts. "The Queen and Constitution", "The Society of Civil Engineers" and "Absent Members" followed the traditional form, but there were variations in those that followed: "To the memory of our departed brothers, Smeaton, Watt, Huddart, Golborne, Rennie, Mylne and others", "Success to waterworks, both public and private, that conduce to the health, the happiness and comfort of mankind" and the sentiment "Dam the canals, blast the minerals, consume the manufactures and disperse the commerce of Great Britain and Ireland".

The toasts and sentiment proved controversial, and some members sought to abolish them. Opinion was divided, but they were dropped before the session ended. At the February meeting three new members were proposed and seconded and they were elected on 4 April; they were Benjamin Baker and Thomas Crampton as ordinary members, and Samuel Pope, QC, as an honorary member. In June, Henry Marc Brunel, Isambard's younger son, was elected an ordinary member and Major General Sir Charles Nugent, KCB, RE, an honorary member.

After dinner on 25 April the President, Sir Frederick Bramwell, observed that three members of the Society, A. Giles, C.W. Siemens and F.A. Abel, had changed their titles and designations without proper notice to the Society. The members present appointed counsel for the Society and for the defendants and formed themselves into a grand jury of 24. The members accused were asked to stand before the members assembled and state whether the allegations were true. The evidence given in the case was of such a confused nature that it was unanimously declared by the jury that the defendants should be given the benefit of the doubt and henceforth be known as Alfred Giles, MP, Sir William Siemens and Sir Frederick Abel. Judgement was given accordingly. Alfred Giles had been the MP for Southampton from 1878 to 1880 and had just regained his seat. The Treasurer reported that four members had received knighthoods during the previous year.

Attendance at the dinners held during the session averaged 14 members and six visitors; there were 36 ordinary members on the Roll. This showed a marked improvement in attendance over the figures reported in 1874 which had given rise to such concern. A new list of members was printed as was to be done every year hereafter. The Rules of the Society were also to be printed annually.

As the 1883 session drew to a close the Treasurer consulted the President about whom he wished to nominate for election as successor and in the first place suggested to Bramwell that he be re-appointed for a second term. Bramwell declined this suggestion, and in a letter to Rennie suggested Woods who he said was universally liked and who would make a charming and acceptable chairman of meetings, although a quiet one, adding "Moreover I am desirous that we should not have a man who will allow the omitted toasts and sentiment to be restored. I feel certain that Woods would oppose any such course, I am not so sure about Hawksley. I don't think he would suggest their restoration but if urged by one or two, he might regard the whole question as one of no importance and might assent". He concluded "if we can keep clear of these toasts for another session, no-one will attempt to revive them and this would, I think, be attained if Woods were made President".

At the opening meeting of the next session the retiring President was absent and Sir Charles Gregory (who had received the KCMG the previous year) occupied the chair. Edward Woods was elected President. Woods had started his career in 1834 as an assistant to John Dixon, Chief Engineer of the Liverpool and Manchester Railway, whom he succeeded two years later. In 1853 he established himself in London as a consulting engineer. His practice was chiefly associated with the construction of railways in South America.

The Treasurer announced that two of the days appointed for meetings, the last Wednesdays of the month, presented difficulties; 27 February was Ash Wednesday and 26 March was the day fixed by the

Institution of Civil Engineers for their annual dinner. It was agreed that no exception should be made for Ash Wednesday but that the March dinner should be held on 19 March. Five new members were elected during the year; Frank McClean, William Preece and Captain Andrew Noble as ordinary members; Admiral Sir Richard Vesey Hamilton and Sir James Allport as honorary members.

At the last meeting of the session Thomas Hawksley was nominated for the presidential election, subject to his consent, which Edward Woods undertook to obtain. Hawksley was elected at the opening meeting of the 1885 session.

Hawksley came from Nottingham where, having attended the High School, he was apprenticed to a local architect and surveyor. In 1830 he was appointed to construct the Trent Waterworks and he served the Waterworks Co. until it was taken over by the city corporation in 1880. At the same time he practised as a consulting engineer in water engineering, a field in which he rapidly built up an international reputation.

At the last dinner of the session an extra meeting was planned. A visit to the experimental lights at the South Foreland was proposed by Sir James Douglass, Engineer-in-Chief, Trinity House. On 8 July members embarked in the Trinity House yacht at Tilbury and arrived at the South Foreland at 4 p.m. The works and experimental lights were inspected. During dinner, which was taken at the Granville Arms Hotel, and afterwards at an observation hut, the lights were seen in action. At 10 p.m. the lights were turned towards Martin Mill Station where the members boarded a special train to return to London.

Meetings were held regularly from 1886 to 1888. Sir Frederick Abel was elected President in 1886; after studying at the Royal Polytechnic Institute and as one of the first students at the newly formed Royal College of Chemistry in 1845, he became a lecturer in chemistry at the RMA, Woolwich, in succession to Michael Faraday. His research in conjunction with Captain Andrew Noble into chemical changes in explosions led to his invention, in collaboration with Sir James Dewar, of cordite.

The President in 1887 was Sir Robert Rawlinson, the Chief Engineer of the Local Government Board. Major General Sir William Crossman, MP, succeeded Rawlinson as President in 1888. He was trained at the RMA, Woolwich, was commissioned in the Royal Engineers in December 1848, and was engaged in the organisation of the Great Exhibition of 1851. In the following year he went to Western Australia to supervise public works by convict labour, but was recalled for the Crimean War. Under the Inspector General of

SOUTH FORELAND.

PROGRAMME, 8th JULY, 1885.

Party to meet in Engine Room between 4 and 5 p.m., inspect Machinery and Apparatus, observe Electric Arc Light from two " DE MERITEN's " Magneto-Electric Machines and a " DE MERITENS' " Lamp. the latter fitted with SIEMENS' Berlin Core Carbons, $40^m/_m$ diameter.

Inspect WIGHAM's Cannel and PINTSCH's Mineral Oil Gas Works, the latter in action.

Inspect High and Low Lighthouses. In the High Lighthouse the arc light from two of " HOLMES's " Magneto-Electric Machines in the focus of the Optical Apparatus for Fixed Light.

Inspect A Experimental Lighthouse. The arc light from a " DE MERITENS' " Machine, in the focus of two Dipping Light Apparatus ; one by Mr. THOMAS STEVENSON, the other by Mr. ALAN BREBNER.

Inspect B, Experimental Lighthouse. One and four 108-jet " WIGHAM " Gas Burners in action.

Inspect C, Experimental Lighthouse. Burners in action :—

One 9-wick Mineral Oil (DOUGLASS).
One 10-ring Gas (do.) Full Power.
One do. do. (do.) Half do

Inspect Photometric Gallery, where a 10-ring Gas Burner (DOUGLASS) will be in action, consuming PINTSCH's Oil Gas, and the Apparatus for Photometric Measurements, including Mr. VERNON HARCOURT's Pentane Gas Apparatus and Photometer.

7.30 to 9.25, at Granville Arms Hotel. Dining and Observing Lights as per Programme of Experiments.

9.30 to 10.0, at No. 2 Hut. Observing Lights as per Programme of Experiments.

10 p.m. Proceed to Martin Mill.

10.30. Proceed by train to London

The South Foreland, 8 July 1885

31 Trinity Street
Borough. S.E.
13 April 1887

G. B. Rennie Esqr.
    Sir
        I beg to acknowledge
the receipt of cheque £2.0.0
for Smeatonian papers —
    I should feel extremely
grateful if you could in
course of time introduce
me to a position where
I could obtain a living
    I have a very small
private income I do not
want much.
    I have been both a
Mechanical & Civil Engineer

I am a good mental
Calculator, quick at figures
and an abstemious man
I can design details of
general machinery or in
other words as a contractor
says I am a "good all round
man" — Your assistance
I shall be grateful for
    I beg to refer you to
James Forrest Esqr C.E
Secretary. Inst C.E.
    I am Sir
    Yours Obedtly
    T. W. Grindle

31 Trinity Street
Borough SE
5 April 1887

The Smeatonian Society of Engineers

To T. Wilson Grindle

To a series of original papers
relating to the proceedings of
the above Society dating from
the year 1805 to 1825
    £2 " 0 " 0

Grindle

Correspondence with T.W. Grindle

Fortifications he planned the defences of dockyards and naval bases at Portsmouth, Portland, Plymouth, etc., and after service in Canada returned to be Assistant Director of Works (Fortifications) at the War Office. He became the Commander Royal Engineers, Southern District, with headquarters at Portsmouth, in 1882, and was promoted to Colonel in 1885, but then resigned to stand for parliament. He was elected as Liberal MP for Portsmouth, retaining his seat until 1892. He was granted the honorary rank of Major General in January 1886.

The lists of members which were revised annually from 1883 (although copies of all the years have not survived) reveal the names of new members and by omission imply the demise or resignation of members of long standing. They record the winning of honours by the more eminent members, evidence of the high regard in which engineers were increasingly being held. The number of Fellows of the Royal Society of London, and of Edinburgh, remained high and the promotion of naval and military members can be traced through successive lists.

When the Society was founded in 1771 its title was the "Society of Civil Engineers" as stated in the Minute Book. When William Mylne started a new Minute Book in 1822 he used the heading "Engineers' Society" in the reports of each session, until in 1869 he changed it to "Smeatonian Society". The rules and regulations issued in 1830 bore the title "Smeatonian Society of Civil Engineers" for the first time, and that has been the title ever since.

In March 1887 the Society was offered a bundle of papers which turned out to be the original manuscripts of the Minutes of meetings and the dinner bills, from the first meeting of the 1805 session on 16 January 1805 to the last in June 1821, and again from 4 February 1824 to April 1825. The first batch was in the handwriting of Robert Mylne until 1811 and John Rennie afterwards, but occasionally they were written and signed by Faden or Vaughan; the later group was by William Mylne. When the papers were offered, Samuel Pope proposed that they be purchased at a price not exceeding two guineas and Robert Mylne secured them for £2, passing the bill to George Rennie, the Treasurer, and adding that the man who sold them, T. W. Grindle, was very badly off. All the documents were faithfully transcribed into the fair Minute Books which George Rennie compiled and maintained.

Great interest was expressed by the members in the early Minutes of the Society and it was decided to have them printed and published. Meanwhile the Treasurer sent members a copy of the Preface to the 1812 edition of Volume 2 of Smeaton's *Reports* because, as he

SOCIETY OF ENGINEERS, 1771.

President—1771-1780   -   -   -   -   -   THOMAS YEOMAN.

  ,,   1781-1782   -   -   -   -   -   CHRISTOPHER PINCHBECK.

  ,,   1783-1792   -   -   -   -   -   ROBERT MYLNE.

SOCIETY OF CIVIL ENGINEERS, 1793.

For 48 years of the Society there was no President but only a Treasurer, but in 1841 it was resolved " That it is expedient that the Society do elect annually a President."

LIST OF PRESIDENTS from 1841 *to* 1887.

1841	SIR JOHN RENNIE.	1865	PETER W. BARLOW.
1842	WILLIAM C. MYLNE.	1866	CHARLES VIGNOLES.
1843	BRYAN DONKIN.	1867	ALFRED GILES.
1844	GEORGE RENNIE.	1868	JOHN FOWLER.
1845	WILLIAM CUBITT.	1869	JOHN PENN.
1846	DR. P. M. ROGET.	1870	LT.-COL. W. JERVOISE, R.E.
1847	ROBERT STEPHENSON.	1871	JOHN BATEMAN.
1848	JOSHUA FIELD.	1872	BRYAN DONKIN.
1849	JOHN TAYLOR.	1873	GEORGE B. RENNIE.
1850	JAMES SIMPSON.	1874	DR. J. PERCY.
1851	THOMAS LLOYD.	1875	WILLIAM H. BARLOW.
1852	JAMES WALKER.	1876	SIR JOSEPH BAZALGETTE.
1853	CHARLES VIGNOLES.	1877	JAMES ABERNETHY.
1854	JOSEPH BAZENDALE.	1878	JAMES BRUNLEES.
1855	SIR JOHN RENNIE.	1879	C. WILLIAM SIEMENS.
1856	ROBERT STEPHENSON.	1880	Not accepted.
1857	JOHN HAWKSHAW.	1881	WARINGTON W. SMITH.
1858	WOLLASTON BLAKE.	1882	GEORGE B. BRUCE.
1859	WILLIAM C. MYLNE.	1883	SIR FREDK. BRAMWELL.
1860	JOHN MURRAY.	1884	EDWARD WOOD.
1861	WILLIAM GRAVATT.	1885	THOMAS HAWKSLEY.
1862	C. HUTTON GREGORY.	1886	SIR FREDERICK ABEL.
1863	COL. J. N. A. SIMMONS, R.E.	1887	SIR ROBERT RAWLINSON.
1864	WILLIAM LINDLEY.	1888	*Major General Sir W. Crofman*
		1889	*J. Clarke Hawkshaw* —

LIST OF TREASURERS.

1771 to 1811 - - - - -	ROBERT MYLNE.
1812 to 1821 - - - - -	JOHN RENNIE.
1822 to 1863 - - - - -	WILLIAM C. MYLNE.
1864 to 1882 - - - - -	ROBERT MYLNE.
1883 to 1888 - - - - -	GEORGE B RENNIE.

List of Presidents and Treasurers, 1888

explained, it gave an account of the early history of the Society and its rules. He appended a copy of the resolution of 15 March 1771 which marked the founding of the Society, and quoted from some of the Minutes of the Society from 1771 to 1792 including early lists of members, concluding with a list of Presidents and Treasurers and the list of members in 1888. In the list of Presidents there are two notable errors; the first title should read "Society of *Civil* Engineers, 1771", and the name of Joseph Nickalls does not appear, the President from 1783 to 1792 being erroneously shown as Robert Mylne.

Although no new members had been elected since 1884, membership in January 1888 stood at 49. Annual subscriptions remained at 30s and the accounts showed a balance in hand of £100 or so. Dinners continued to be held at the Freemasons Tavern and the average attendance at dinner was 13 members: there were invariably two or three visitors.

There were three new ordinary members elected in 1888, Sir Bradford Leslie, Richard Sennett and William Anderson, and two honorary members. Sir Bradford Leslie had been a pupil of Isambard Brunel and continued to work for him on the railways and the construction of SS *Great Eastern*. Through Brunel he went to India on railway and bridge construction. Richard Sennett was the Engineer-in-Chief, Admiralty (a civilian appointment), having been appointed the year before. He retired from the Admiralty in 1889 and became a director of Maudslay, Son and Field. William Anderson, after studying at Kings College, London, became a pupil of William Fairbairn in the construction of machinery; he later worked with Sir Frederick Abel and designed the machines to make the new smokeless explosive, cordite. In 1889 he was appointed Director-General of Ordnance Factories.

In 1889 the President was John Clarke Hawkshaw, the only son of Sir John, who went to Westminster School and Trinity College, Cambridge. In 1865 he became a pupil of his father and a partner with his father and Harrison Hayter in 1870; they were mainly engaged in maritime works in the UK and South America.

Richard Boxall Grantham was 84 when he succeeded Hawkshaw as President in 1890. He was a pupil of Augustus Pugin the architect. His father, a civil engineer, had worked under John Rennie in Ireland and Richard joined him there in 1823. Together they worked under George and John Rennie, surveying the London and Birmingham line, part of the Great Western railway. Richard worked with the Rennie brothers and Isambard Brunel on railways until in his own practice he broadened into land drainage and reclamation, sewerage and sewage disposal.

In June 1890 Field Marshal Sir John Simmons was invited to become the President for a second term. He expressed his gratitude for the invitation but hesitated, he said, for two reasons; his absence abroad for so long had put him out of touch with the members and also, having suffered attacks of fever, he was obliged to be careful: but in the end he accepted. As a captain he had been elected an honorary member in 1851. He served as President in 1863 while stationed at Aldershot, when he had reached the rank of Colonel. In 1865 he became Director of the RE establishment at Chatham and as a Major General and then Lieutenant General, he was the Governor of the RMA, Woolwich, from 1869 until he was appointed Inspector General of Fortifications in 1875. He was the Governor of Malta from 1884 to 1888.

The new members who joined in 1890 were William Henry White, the Director of Naval Construction, Admiralty, who had been one of the first students to enter the Royal School of Naval Architecture and Marine Engineering at South Kensington when it opened in 1864; Francis William Webb, Chief Mechanical Engineer of the London, North Western Railway; and George Cunningham, a consulting engineer in Edinburgh.

At the first meeting of the 1891 session the death of Robert William Mylne, Treasurer 1864–82 was announced. He had died at his residence, Home Lodge, Great Amwell, Herts., on 2 July 1890. His death brought to an end a period of 119 years in which three generations of the Mylne family, descending from Robert Mylne (1734–1811) one of the Society's founders, had served the Society.

At the end of the session an additional meeting was held. The members of the Society and Council Members of the Institution of Civil Engineers paid a joint visit to the workshops of the LNWR at Crewe. Arrangements were made by Francis Webb, and the railway company provided special trains and an excellent lunch and dinner.

When the next session opened on 27 January 1892 the elected President, John Wolfe Barry was in the chair. He was the youngest son of Sir Charles Barry, the architect of the rebuilt Houses of Parliament. From Trinity College, Glenalmond, and Kings College, London, he became the pupil of Sir John Hawkshaw, and worked on the bridges and stations at Charing Cross and Cannon Street. He set up his own practice as a consulting engineer in 1867, and his work included the underground railways (working with Hawkshaw) and the bridges at Blackfriars and Kew. He was the engineer for the docks at Immingham, Barry and Newport, and for railways in South Wales.

The printing and publication of the early Minutes of the Society, decided upon in 1888, took some time to arrange. In 1892 Messrs

Smeatonian Society of Civil Engineers

Freemasons' Tavern,
Great Queen Street
Lincolns Inn Fields,
London, W.C.

(seal: SPIERS & POND LIMITED / CENTRAL OFFICES / LUDGATE, E.C.)

1889

Jan 30	16 Dinners	10/—	8	. .
	2 Sherry	8/–	16	.
	1 Rudesheimer		5	—
	1 Chablis		4	
	5 Pommery	11/6	2 17 6	
	2 Clicquot	10/6	1 1	.
	4 Leoville 77	8/–	1 12	.
	1 La Rose		5	—
	7 Minerals		3 6	
	50 Cigars	6	1 5	—
	Cigarettes		2	
	1 Punch		5	—
	1 Madeira		8	
			17 4	—
	By Cash		8 15	—
			£ 8 9	—

14 Fe...

J. W. Taylor

Dinner at Freemasons Tavern, 20 January 1889

Vacher & Son, printers and bookbinders, produced 60 copies of the facsimile of the original 1771 Minute Book, at a cost to the Society of £43 18s 4d; 33 copies were taken up by the members at 5s each.

Sir James Brunlees died in June 1892. He had completed the Mersey Railway and its tunnel under the Mersey, jointly with Douglas Fox, in 1886 and both had been knighted. Two honorary members, the Duke of Sutherland and Sir James Allport, had also died. The following year there were two more deaths: Thomas Hawksley and Bryan Donkin.

In 1893 an honorary member was once again elected President. He was Samuel Pope, QC, born in Manchester, who studied at London University and was called to the bar by the Middle Temple in 1858. At first he practised in Manchester but moved to London in 1865 and became a leader of the parliamentary Bar.

Towards the end of the session a move to another venue was suggested and the President invited all the members of the Society to a trial dinner at Edouard Willis's Restaurant in King Street, St James's, on Tuesday 25 July. The event met with general approval and arrangements were made to hold the Society's dinners there at least for the next session. So after 70 years of continuous patronage of the Freemasons Tavern, the venue changed.

The immediate result was an increase in the cost of dinners. This, combined with a drop in income resulting from a fall in the number of members from 50 in 1891 to 40, led to financial difficulties. From a balance in hand of £61 7s 6d at the end of 1893 there was a deficit of £5 19s 6d by January 1896. The Treasurer suggested three possible remedies; an increase in the annual subscription, an increase in the number of members, or a reduction in expenditure. In January an increase in subscription to two guineas was approved, and it was agreed that the membership be increased to 50 once more, by the election of six new ordinary members and four honorary members. By January there were 37 members and 11 honorary members, leaving two vacancies still to be filled. This did not bring immediate relief and it was 1901 before a credit balance was achieved once again.

The President who followed Samuel Pope was Sir Benjamin Baker. After attending Cheltenham Grammar School he served a four year apprenticeship with H. H. Price at Neath Abbey Ironworks. On moving to London in 1860 he worked on the construction of Grosvenor Road railway bridge and Victoria Station. In 1861 he joined Sir John Fowler and was his partner from 1875 until Fowler's death in 1898. As assistant to Fowler, he was employed on the Metropolitan (Inner Circle) Railway from 1861 and in 1869 on the District Railway from Westminster to the City. Fowler and Baker acted as consultants for the first tube railway, the City and South London line, opened in 1890, and with J. H. Greathead were joint engineers for the Central Line. Fowler's and Baker's great achievement was the Forth Railway Bridge, and when it was completed in 1890 Sir John Fowler received a baronetcy and Baker was awarded the KCMG.

Henry Marc Brunel, the President in 1895, was the younger of Isambard's two sons; the elder son became a barrister. Henry was 17 years of age when his father died. From Harrow School he went to King's College, London, and then became a pupil, first with Sir William Armstrong & Co., Elswick, and then with John Hawkshaw, continuing as his assistant until 1870. Under Hawkshaw he worked on docks and railways and took soundings in the English Channel for the proposed Channel Tunnel. In 1878 he entered into partnership with John Wolfe Barry.

At the meeting on 30 January 1895, an amendment to the Rules was proposed by Sir Frederick Bramwell and seconded by Alexander Binnie. Their purpose was to ensure that a candidate for election to membership was not present when his candidature was first brought before the members and that he would not be present when the ballot took place. The new Rule was added when the Rules were reprinted in 1899.

Brunel was followed as President by Sir Douglas Galton. From Rugby School and the RMA, Woolwich, he was commissioned in the Royal Engineers in 1840. He served under General Sir Charles Pasley until posted to Malta, then to Gibraltar and on returning home in 1846 joined the Ordnance Survey. He was involved with the Railway Commission and the Royal Commission on the application of iron to railway structures. In 1857 he was one of the three government referees, with James Simpson and Blackwell, who reported on Bazalgette's plans for the drainage of London.

Two years later he was chairman of a government committee investigating submarine telegraph cables after the failure of the Atlantic cable in 1858. Galton returned to military duties in 1860 but two years later was put on the half-pay list and appointed Permanent Under-Secretary of State for War. After seven years he was transferred to the Office of Works as Director of Public Works and Buildings, from which post he retired in 1875.

The dinners at Willis's Restaurant proved popular. Members paid 10s and visitors had to be paid for at 15s. The subscription in 1897 was £2 and there were 37 ordinary members and 11 honorary members, two short of the maximum permitted number of 50. Frank McClean, the only son of J. R. McClean, was elected President. He was

LIST OF THE MEMBERS
OF THE
SMEATONIAN SOCIETY OF CIVIL ENGINEERS.

FOUNDED 1771.

JANUARY, 1901.

Date of Election		
1860	GEORGE BANKS RENNIE	20, Lowndes Street.
1869	SIR FREDERICK J. BRAMWELL, Bart., D.C.L., LL.D., F.R.S.	5, Great George Street.
1870	SIR GEORGE B. BRUCE	3, Victoria Street, S.W.
,,	SIR ALEXANDER MEADOWS RENDEL, K.C.I.E., M.A.	8, Great George Street.
1872	EDWARD WOODS	6a, Victoria Street.
1876	J. CLARKE HAWKSHAW, M.A.	33, Great George Street.
1879	SIR J. WOLFE BARRY, K.C.B., LL.D., F.R.S.	21, Delahay Street.
,,	FRANCIS STEVENSON	Euston Station, Euston Square.
1883	SIR BENJAMIN BAKER, K.C.M.G., LL.D., F.R.S.	2, Queen Square Place.
,,	H. M. BRUNEL	21, Delahay Street.
1884	FRANK McCLEAN, M.A.	Rusthall House, Tunbridge Wells.
,,	SIR W. H. PREECE, K.C.B., F.R.S.	13, Queen Anne's Gate, S.W.
,,	CAPTAIN SIR ANDREW NOBLE (late R.A.), K.C.B., F.R.S.	Jesmond Dene House, Newcastle-on-Tyne.
1888	SIR BRADFORD LESLIE, K.C.I.E.	The Moat, Harrow-on-the-Hill.
1889	SIR W. H. WHITE, K.C.B., LL.D., F.R.S.	Admiralty.
1890	F. W. WEBB	Chester Place, Crewe.
1891	JAMES MANSERGH	5, Victoria Street, Westminster.
1892	PERCY G. B. WESTMACOTT	Rose Mount, Sunning Hill, Berks.
,,	SIR A. R. BINNIE	Spring Gardens, S.W.
1894	GEORGE CHATTERTON	6, The Sanctuary, Westminster.
,,	ALEXANDER SIEMENS	12, Queen Anne's Gate, S.W.
,,	GEORGE N. ABERNETHY	1, Delahay Street, S.W.
1896	GEORGE FREDERICK DEACON	32, Victoria Street, S.W.
,,	W. R. GALBRAITH	20, Victoria Street, S.W.
,,	THOMAS FORSTER BROWN	15, Victoria Street, Westminster.
,,	A. B. W. KENNEDY, LL.D., F.R.S.	17, Victoria Street, Westminster, S.W.
,,	SIR EDWARD HAMER CARBUTT, Bart.	19, Hyde Park Gardens.
,,	JOHN MAIR RUMLEY	43, Palace Court, W.
,,	C. A. BRERETON	21, Delahay Street.
1897	W. MATTHEWS, C.M.G.	Westminster Chambers, 9, Victoria Street.
,,	CHARLES HAWKSLEY	30, Great George Street.
1898	HORACE BELL	28, Victoria Street, Westminster, S.W.
,,	GEORGE R. JEBB	Fairfield, Great Barr, Birmingham.
,,	W. C. UNWIN, F.R.S.	7, Palace Gate Mansions, Kensington, W.
1899	SIR JOHN A. DURSTON, R.N., K.C.B.	Admiralty.
,,	PHILIP WATTS, F.R.S.	Elswick, Newcastle-on-Tyne.
,,	F. E. ROBERTSON	8, Gt. George Street, Westminster.
1900	JOHN ISAAC THORNEYCROFT, F.R.S.	Eyot Villa, Chiswick Mall.
,,	FRANCIS ELGAR, LL.D., F.R.S.	18, York Terrace.
,,	SAXTON WILLIAM ARMSTRONG NOBLE	The Grove, Jesmond, Newcastle-on-Tyne.

HONORARY MEMBERS.

1861	FIELD-MARSHAL SIR J. L. A. SIMMONS, R.E., G.C.B., G.C.M.G.	United Service Club, Pall Mall.
1877	SIR FREDERICK A. ABEL, Bart., K.C.B., D.C.L., F.R.S.	2, Whitehall Court.
1878	MAJOR-GEN. SIR W. CROSSMAN, R.E., K.C.M.G.,	United Service Club, Pall Mall.
1885	SAMUEL POPE, Q.C.	74, Ashley Gardens.
1894	JAMES DEWAR, M.A., LL.D., F.R.S.	Royal Institution, Albemarle Street.
1896	SIR CHARLES WILSON, R.E., K.C.M.G.	9, Warwick Square.
,,	A. COMMON, LL.D., F.R.S.	Eaton Rise, Ealing.
,,	SIR JAMES THOMPSON	9, Victoria Street, S.W.

List of members, 1901

educated at Westminster School, Glasgow University and Trinity College, Cambridge. After serving his pupillage with John Hawkshaw he joined the partnership of McClean and Stileman in 1862. At the age of 33 he retired and set up an observatory at Tunbridge Wells to pursue his hobby of astronomy. He went on to enter parliament.

William Henry Preece was elected President the following year. He went to King's College School and King's College, London. His early practical training was at the Royal Institution under Michael Faraday. He then entered the office of Edwin Clark, the former assistant to Robert Stephenson on the Britannia and Conway Bridges, who had become the Engineer-in-Chief of the Electric Telegraph Co. Preece worked for the telegraph companies, and when they were taken over by the government he joined the Post Office Telegraphic Service, retiring as Engineer-in-Chief in 1899 to become a consultant.

In 1899 Sir Andrew Noble became the President. He had entered the RMA, Woolwich, as a cadet in 1847, was commissioned in the Royal Artillery in 1849, and served for 11 years, mainly abroad. On returning to England he worked with Frederick Abel on explosives, and was involved in the trials of W.G. Armstrong's rifled, breechloading field gun. In 1860 Noble left the army to join Armstrong. He became Vice-Chairman of Sir W.G. Armstrong & Co in 1882 and Chairman of Sir W.G. Armstrong Whitworth & Co. Ltd when Lord Armstrong died in 1900. Andrew Noble's sister, Georgina, married Isambard the elder son of Isambard Kingdom Brunel, the barrister and Chancellor of the Diocese of Ely.

The President in 1900 was Sir William White, who after serving at the Admiralty from 1867 to 1883 joined Sir W.G. Armstrong & Co. as designer and manager of their new warship building yard at Elswick. Two years later he returned to the Admiralty as Director of Naval Construction.

Francis William Webb was elected President for 1901. At the age of 15 he became a pupil of Francis Trevithick, at that time the locomotive superintendent of the LNWR. At the end of his pupillage he entered the drawing office; in February 1859 he was appointed chief draughtsman and in 1861 works manager. He became the manager of the Bolton Iron and Steel works, serving for five years before returning to Crewe to become Chief Mechanical Engineer on the LNWR. He was a great benefactor of the town of Crewe where most of his life was spent.

The invitations for the first dinner of the 1901 session had already been sent out when news of the Queen's illness reached the Treasurer. When she died on 22 January, the President ordered its cancellation; it was a time of national mourning.

Chapter Six

1901–1930

Dinners were resumed at Willis's Restaurant in February 1901 with Francis Webb in the Chair. Two members had died, Lord Armstrong and Dr William Pole, and two were elected, the Rt Hon. William Pirrie of Harland and Wolff Ltd, Belfast, and James Inglis of the Great Western Railway. Dr Ludwig Mond, the chemist, was elected an honorary member, and a new list of members was prepared for 1902. For the 1902 session, Sir James Dewar, who had been an honorary member since 1894, was President. He held the Jacksonian Chair of Natural Experimental Philosophy at Cambridge from 1875, and two years later acquired the additional chair of Fullerian Professor of Chemistry at the Royal Institution. His work with Sir Frederick Abel in the government committee on explosives led to their joint invention of cordite. His liquefaction of hydrogen was a step towards the practical achievement of absolute zero temperature.

To celebrate the coronation of King Edward VII, the Society held a special dinner in August. This put an extra strain on the Society's funds. At the end of the session there was a deficit of £18 5s 0d and in order to clear it an additional charge of £1 per member was levied. The charge for a member's guest was also increased, to one guinea, and the annual subscription raised to £2 10s 0d from January 1904.

George Banks Rennie, who by 1902 was the longest serving member, resigned from the post of Treasurer which he had held since 1883. His son, John Assheton Rennie, was elected an ordinary member and appointed Treasurer in his place, and the secretarial work was undertaken by J. Perry in the offices of Messrs. G. Rennie & Co., Thames Street, Greenwich.

At the first meeting in 1903, James Mansergh was proposed for President. He was the water engineer who had pioneered the Elan Valley scheme to supply water to Birmingham. He declined owing to pressure of work, and Percy Westmacott was elected. Westmacott came from Edinburgh and served his apprenticeship with a firm of marine engineers. He joined W.G. Armstrong & Co., Elswick, in

1851, became works manager two years later and a partner in 1863; when the firm was incorporated as Sir W.G. Armstrong Whitworth & Co. Ltd. in 1897 he was appointed Managing Director.

Mansergh declined nomination again in 1904, and Sir Alexander Binnie was elected President. Binnie had been the Chief Engineer of the London County Council until 1902, when he retired and went into practice as a consulting engineer, founding the firm now known as Binnie & Partners.

The President in 1905 was George Chatterton, a former student of Trinity College, Dublin and an ex-pupil of Sir Joseph Bazalgette, whose daughter he married. He practised in the field of municipal and water engineering; his works included the drainage of the City of Dublin.

At the first dinner of the 1905 session Dr Leonard Walden of New York was among the visitors. Responding to the toast of the guests, he described in an amusing speech the American plans to build the Panama Canal, a subject of great interest in view of the earlier failure of the French attempt.

The time-honoured toasts once again came under review. They had been reintroduced at some time after their suppression in Bramwell's day. The loyal toast was now "The King and Constitution", of course, but the lengthy toast "To the memory of our late worthy brothers" was shortened, naming only Smeaton, Mylne, Watt and Rennie as it had been in the 1820s. The rest of the toasts and the sentiment remained unaltered. Attendance during the session had been good, and the effect of raising the price of entertaining a guest had increased the ratio of members to guests which was stated to be an advantage.

The overall improvement in the financial state of the Society made it possible to reduce the annual subscription to two guineas. The move to Willis's gave the Society the use of the superior dining and reception rooms of Willis's Club, which the members agreed "was much more commodious and congenial".

Having no premises of its own, the Society had difficulty in ensuring a safe resting place for its possessions. Gifts included some items which formerly belonged to John Rennie; a pair of spectacles in their case, a set of mathematical instruments and two volumes of Belidor's "Architecture Hydraulique". These and two of the Society's early Minute Books were handed over to the Institution of Civil Engineers for safe-keeping, under arrangements made by Sir Alexander Binnie with the Secretary of the Institution.

Mansergh died in June 1905, and Alexander Siemens was elected President for 1906. He was born in Hanover and was a kinsman of the Siemens brothers whose works at Charlton he joined in 1867. He worked in the Middle East, constructing telegraph lines, and then in 1870–71 he fought in the Franco-Prussian War winning the Iron Cross. After the war he returned to England as a pupil of Sir William Siemens, and became a naturalized British subject in 1878. In the following year he took over the electric lighting department of Siemens Bros.

A book of portraits and signatures of all the Past Presidents was proposed, and a suitable album was purchased. It was to be no bigger than the old Minute Book and an appeal was launched for portraits no larger than 6in. x 4in. There was a good response; engravings were found of some of the earliest Presidents and the descendants of others offered copies from their family records. More recent Presidents produced their photographs. The intention was that, when compiled, copies of the album would be printed so that each member could have one.

The final item of business at the last meeting of the session was the election of George Abernethy as President for 1907, after which the meeting adjourned to the Conversazione of the Institution of Civil Engineers. Abernethy had been a student at King's College, London, and spent a year at Sir W.G. Armstrong & Co. works, followed by pupillage under his father, James. He became a partner with his father, engaging in maritime and dock work.

A meeting of Colonial Premiers was due to be held in London in 1907, and in April the Treasurer wrote to the Secretary of State for the Colonies, on behalf of the President and members, to invite the Premiers to dinner. It was hoped that this would provide a suitable opportunity to bring together the Premiers and the engineers of this country who were heavily involved in colonial development. In his reply, Lord Elgin, the Secretary of State, expressed his appreciation for the invitation and his sympathy with the object of such a meeting, but regretted that advantage could not be taken of it, as there was no free night left on which the dinner could take place.

Frank Elgar was the last to leave after the dinner on 29 May and found only one hat on the stand: it was not his own. It bore the initials "A.S." inside and he traced it to a guest of Sir John Durston, a Mr Spyre, who responded by exchanging it for the one he had taken mistakenly. But that turned out not to be Elgar's either. Elgar wrote to the Treasurer, apologising for troubling him and enquiring whether he had heard from the possessor of his hat, which could be identified by the name of the maker "Lincoln Bennett". Whether his hat was ever restored to him and by whom is, regrettably, not recorded.

Sir William Preece, George Jebb, Edward Woods, Francis Webb and Harry Woods

John A. Rennie, Esq.

EDOUARD WILLIS RESTAURANT, LIMITED.
KING STREET,
ST. JAMES'S, S.W.

TELEGRAPHIC ADDRESS:
"EDOUARD, LONDON."

TELEPHONE NO.
5221 GERRARD.

Smeatonian Society

1907

			£	s	d
May 29.	27. Dinners		14	3	6
	12 — 70 dd.		9	12	0
	5 — 83		1	0	0
	3 — 95		1	4	0
	2 — 108			16	0
	2 — 107		1	0	0
	Whisky			2	0
	Apollinaris			9	0
	Perrier			8	0
	Liqueurs		1	9	0
	Cigars & Cigarettes		1	19	6
	Waiters			10	0
		£	32	13	0
			18	10	0
		£	14	3	0

Received by Cheque £14 . 3 . 0
A. H. Hunnington
manager.

Balance due

With Compliments to

Dinner at Willis's Restaurant, 29 May 1907

The boost in membership to a maximum of 50 in 1896 had the desired effect of increasing the annual income and improving the financial position of the Society, but it gave only temporary relief to the pressure on admissions. Membership was highly prized, and vacancies were very limited. Candidates properly proposed and seconded seemed rarely to have failed to be elected, and rejection became even more unlikely when three black balls instead of one became necessary to exclude a candidate.

It was claimed that a very considerable change had come about in recent years and that many of the elections had been carried out in a "hurried and somewhat informal manner". Members were not to be discouraged from putting forward those they thought suitable, but greater deliberation was desirable, and when vacancies were few and there were many candidates, some form of selection was thought to be needed. So instead of all candidates proposed and seconded being put to the ballot, in future proposals would be considered by a committee, comprising the President and the five Past Presidents immediately preceding him, who would put forward to the ballot only those they selected and recommended. Rule VII was amended and a new Rule XVII added, authorising the new procedure and giving the Presidents' Committee additional powers to consider and decide upon any matters referred to it.

The new procedure operated in 1908, when out of a list of seven candidates, three were recommended by the committee and duly elected by the members; they were Edward Pritchard Martin, metallurgist, a director of Guest Keen and Nettlefold Ltd.; Sir Thomas Matthews, Engineer-in-Chief, Trinity House; and William Barton Worthington, Engineer-in-Chief, Midland Railway. It was agreed that under the new procedure the names of the unsuccessful candidates would not be divulged by the committee.

Thomas Forster Brown was elected to be the next President, but he died before taking office and Sir Alexander Kennedy was elected in his place. Until 1889 Kennedy had been the Professor of Engineering at University College, London. In that year he set up his consulting practice as Kennedy and Jenkin, the firm later became Kennedy and Donkin, with Sydney Bryan Donkin as a partner.

Sir Alexander Rendel wrote to say he felt compelled to resign owing to his advanced years. He continued his work, however, and when his partner F.E. Robertson died in 1912 he took into partnership Frederick Palmer and Seymour Tritton, who, with his sons, carried on the practice as Rendel, Palmer and Tritton.

In June 1908 Willis's Rooms were partly destroyed by fire and the last dinner of the session was held at Princes Restaurant, Piccadilly.

The President suggested that the Society dine there in future, as they were given a good dinner. The members agreed that Princes Restaurant was "superior".

George Deacon was elected President for 1909; after studying at Glasgow and having taken part in the laying of the Trans-Atlantic cable in SS *Great Eastern* in 1865, he settled in Liverpool, and for a time was the borough engineer. He set up his own practice at Westminster in 1890. Only a few days before the final dinner of the session, he died suddenly. The dinner was postponed until 14 July, when Sir Alexander Binnie took the chair. In addition to the President, the Society lost several members during 1909; George Banks Rennie, the ex-Treasurer; Sir George Bruce, Past President, and three other members died, and Sir Bradford Leslie retired.

The Presidents' Committee met several times and finally recommended the election of four ordinary members and one honorary member: Robert White, a mechanical engineer; Anthony George Lyster, the second son of George and, like his father, a docks engineer; Walter Hunter, a water engineer, and Engineer Vice Admiral Sir Henry Oram, were nominated as ordinary members with John Hutton Balfour Browne, KC, as an honorary member; all were duly elected. The new procedure, it was said, was working very smoothly. At the July meeting the railway engineer Cuthbert Brereton was elected as successor to George Deacon, to take office immediately and for the following year. He had been Sir John Wolfe Barry's partner from 1893 to 1909 and had just set up his own independent practice in Westminster.

In view of the deaths of George Deacon, Dr Ludwig Mond and Berkeley Paget, the Presidents' Committee at its first meeting in 1910 advised the members that there were three vacancies to fill. They recommended the election of Sir Thomas Wrightson, Bart, as an ordinary member; Sir David Gill, the astronomer, and Edward Honoratus Lloyd, KC, as honorary members. They were duly elected at the next meeting. Sir Thomas Wrightson had been a pupil of Sir John Fowler and of Lord Armstrong, his cousin.

The dinner on 27 April 1910 was devoted to the entertainment of the "literary and artistic" professions. Among the distinguished guests were Sir Aston Webb, RA, Sir Seymour Lucas, RA, Fred Roe, E.T. Reed "Punch", W.H. Thornycroft, RA, R. Talbot Kelly, Sir Alfred East, ARA, David Murray, RA, and William L. Wyllie, RA. The dinner was well attended and some good speeches delivered, but not without some plain speaking. David Murray's allegation of a lack of artistic appreciation by some civil engineers in the design of bridges was judged to be "a little severe".

SMEATONIAN SOCIETY OF CIVIL ENGINEERS

.. MENU ..

Royal Whitstable Natives
Hors-d'Œuvre à la Russe

Consommé aux Ailerons
Crême Lamballe

Suprême de Sole à la Parisienne
Friture à la Murat

Ris de Veau à la Banquière

Selle d'Agneau Flambée
Pommes Nouvelles à la Menthe
Haricots Verts à l'Anglaise

Bécasses en Casserole au Champagne
Salade de Saison

Fonds d'Artichauts à la Florentine

Bombe Glacée Rosolios
Brouette de Fanfreluches

Canapés Charles Quint

Dessert.   Café

Princes' Hotel & Restaurant,
Piccadilly, W.   27th January, 1909.

Dinner at Princes Restaurant, 27 January 1909

The May dinner was postponed when it was learned that the King had died. Once again there was a period of national mourning. The President, Cuthbert Brereton, died suddenly in September and the deaths of George Chatterton, Past President, and Graham Harris were reported; William Galbraith resigned on account of age, making at least four vacancies to be filled in 1911.

Sir William Matthews was invited to accept nomination for President in 1911, but he declined. Although he had been a member for a long time, he had only attended one of the dinners; he had not resigned, he said, because a great many valued friends were members, but he felt he could not take up the position of President.

Charles Hawksley, who was elected President, was the son of Thomas; after leaving University College, London, he became a pupil under his father and in 1866 joined him as partner. He convened a meeting of the Presidents' Committee at his house on 23 January; those attending were Sir Alexander Binnie, Sir Alexander Kennedy, Alexander Siemens, George Abernethy and John Rennie, the Treasurer. The first item on the agenda was to select six new members from the list of 18 names which had been formally proposed and seconded in writing in accordance with the rules. Sir Alexander Kennedy proposed that the six should all be ordinary members and that the number of honorary members be increased without decreasing the number of ordinary members. The six candidates nominated were Dr John Henry Tudsbery Tudsbery, Secretary of the Institution of Civil Engineers; Hay Frederick Donaldson, Chief Superintendant of Ordnance Factories; Sir Frederick Upcott, Director of Indian Railways; John Audley Frederick Aspinall, General Manager, Lancashire and Yorkshire Railway; Dugald Clerk, Director of Engineering Research, Admiralty; and Dr James Alfred Ewing, engineer and physicist.

The committee proposed a modification to Rule V to advance the election of the President, allowing him more time before the start of the session to arrange his affairs, by substituting the word "last" in place of the word "first" and adding "for the following session" after the word "President". Rule XI was also amended so that the amount of the annual contribution would be determined each year by the Presidents' Committee and not by the members attending the first meeting of the session. A new Rule was added which limited the total number of ordinary and honorary members together to not more than 60.

Sir Alexander Kennedy pointed out that as constituted the Presidents' Committee consisted of the President for the session and as many of the five immediately preceding Past Presidents as were alive; in January 1911 there were only three and there could conceivably be none. It was probably the original intention, and was certainly desirable, that the number of committee members should not fall below five. He recommended therefore that the committee be formed by the five *living* Past Presidents immediately preceding the President.

The committee's recommendations were approved by the members, and it was also agreed that when a large party of about 20 or more was expected at dinner, seating arrangements should be made beforehand. The dinner held on 29 March was to be specifically for the entertainment of guests from the naval and military services; 18 attended, including Engineer Vice Admiral Sir John Durston, Engineer Vice Admiral Sir Henry Oram and Sir Philip Watts of the Admiralty. Among the guests were Rear Admiral the Hon. Alexander Bethell, Rear Admiral H.G. King Hall, Colonel Sir Reginald Hennell, Colonel the Hon. T. F. Fremantle, Colonel Bonham Carter, Major Carmichael, RE, Major T. W. Pringle, RE, and Captain M. H. P. R. Sankey.

The President in 1912 was George Robert Jebb, who had served his pupillage on the Chester line of the Great Western Railway. He was engaged in canal and maritime projects as well as in railways. A meeting of the Presidents' Committee was held on 24 January in a room at the Institution of Civil Engineers. In addition to the President and the Treasurer it was attended by Past Presidents Sir Alexander Siemens, George Abernethy and Charles Hawksley.

The number of members having been increased to 60, within this number the committee considered that there should be 48 ordinary members and 12 honorary members, but recommended that the full number should not be made up for the present; two new ordinary members and five or six honorary members were thought to be sufficient for the time being. In the first category as members they recommended Godfred Midgley Taylor, the son of John Taylor and a partner in the firm of John Taylor & Sons, and Sir James Swinburne, the consulting electrical engineer who with Dr Backeland produced Bakelite and pioneered the plastics industry. As honorary members they proposed Sir Archibald Geikie, geologist; Captain Sir Herbert Acton Blake, RN, Deputy Master of Trinity House; Sir Gilbert Henry Claughton, Chairman LNWR; Colonel Sir Thomas Hungerford Holdich of the Indian Survey; and Sir Oliver Lodge, physicist. The Treasurer was asked to approach Sir Ernest Shackleton, the explorer, with a view to honorary membership. Sir Ernest accepted nomination, but Sir Oliver Lodge declined. The nominees were duly elected by the members at the next meeting.

The procedure for the election of members resulted in an ever-increasing list of candidates, as new names were added and only a limited number of vacancies filled. It was agreed, however, that the names of candidates who had not been selected by the committee for election would be taken off the waiting list after a period of four years.

There was mounting criticism of the Rules. Sir William White wrote to the President on 17 February 1912, making suggestions for their improvement and advocating a return to a procedure whereby all candidates for election to membership, not just those selected by the committee, would be entered in the ballot. His letter was sent to all members and their comments and additional suggestions sought. The replies were referred to an *ad hoc* committee, to which Sir John Wolfe Barry, Sir James Dewar and John Balfour Browne, KC, were appointed. The amendments to the Rules which the *ad hoc* committee proposed were discussed by the members on 20 May and formally adopted at the meeting on 29 May, which was very well attended. The resolutions which brought the changes into effect were passed on 26 June, the last meeting of the session.

The most important changes in the Rules affected the procedure for the election of new members. No longer would they be selected by the Presidents' Committee, but a list of all those proposed and seconded would be sent to the members by the Treasurer (now referred to as "Hon. Treasurer") not less than seven days before the AGM. Printed proposal forms were introduced to facilitate this. To be elected, a candidate must poll two-thirds of the votes of the members present. Some thought this should be three-quarters, as in the case of the Royal Society, but in the end, two-thirds prevailed. If after the first ballot vacancies remained unfilled, further ballots would take place until all the places were filled. There were to be no more than 48 ordinary members and 12 honorary members. Other changes were that the President would be elected at the AGM, and that the annual contributions would be determined by the Treasurer and not by the Presidents' Committee; in fact the committee ceased to have any specific function under the revised Rules. When amending the Rules to incorporate these changes the opportunity was taken to re-edit them.

Professor William Cawthorne Unwin was elected President for 1913. A graduate of London University by private study, he was appointed an assistant to Sir William Fairbairn at Manchester in 1856, and became the manager of the engine department of Fairbairn Engineering Co. later. In 1869 he lectured on marine engineering at the Royal School of Naval Architecture and Marine Engineering, and when the Royal Indian Engineering College, Coopers Hill, opened in

Dinner at Princes Restaurant, 29 March 1911

1871 he was appointed Professor of Hydraulics and Mechanical Engineering. When the Central Institute of the City and Guilds of London was completed, Unwin was the Professor of Civil and Mechanical Engineering, and on its incorporation into London University he became the first London University Professor of Engineering.

The new Rules for the election of members came into operation in 1913 and to comply with them the Hon. Treasurer sent out a circular to all members informing them that there would be four vacancies in the list for ordinary members and two for honorary members. Ten names were proposed and seconded for ordinary membership and two for honorary membership. Ballots took place at the last meeting of the session, 23 June, which was designated the Annual General Meeting. Voting papers replaced the former ballot box.

Five ballots were conducted to decide upon the four new ordinary members, the stumbling block being the two-thirds rule. Twenty two members being present, at least 15 votes were necessary for election. In the first ballot only one candidate reached this number and in the second ballot there was one more; the third and fourth ballots produced no results, and in the fifth ballot two were declared successful. After the meeting objections were raised, it being pointed out that although those who received the greatest number of votes in the fifth ballot were declared elected, one of them still fell short of the two-thirds of the votes of those present required by the Rules. The President took the next opportunity to apologise for this oversight and the objection to the ballot was then withdrawn, with the observation that a sixth ballot, had it been held, was unlikely to have produced a different result. The objector expressed the view however, that a simple election, in which members would vote for the candidates they knew and supported, was to be preferred to the system which required members to vote for a fixed number of candidates, whether they knew them or not. The general opinion was that the system so recently adopted should be continued.

The four newly elected ordinary members were Colonel Sir Percy Girouard, RE, the railway engineer and colonial administrator, a former Governor of the British East Africa Proctectorate and now a director of Sir W.G. Armstrong Whitworth & Co. Ltd; Sir Archibald Denny, Naval Constructor, a partner in the family firm, William Denny & Bros. Shipbuilders; Edward Bazzand Ellington, a former pupil of John Penn & Son, marine engineers, Greenwich, Chief Engineer of the General Hydraulic Power Co.; and Basil Mott, the mining engineer, a partner with Sir Benjamin Baker. After Baker's death in 1907 Mott carried on the practice with David Hay and David Anderson; the firm now bears their names. Major General Sir Charles Frederick Hadden, President of the Ordnance Board, and Sir William Crookes, Secretary of the Royal Institution, the only candidates for the two vacancies, were elected honorary members.

Before the meeting closed, Sir Philip Watts was elected President for 1914. As a shipwright apprentice at Portsmouth Dockyard he won a place at the Royal School of Naval Architecture and Marine Engineering, South Kensington, in 1866. After experience at the Admiralty and in dockyards, he left government service to succeed Sir William White as general manager of the shipyard of Sir W.G. Armstrong & Co., Elswick. In 1902 Watts succeeded White again as Director of Naval Construction, Admiralty, a post from which he retired in 1912.

The AGM of the 1914 session was held on the afternoon of 24 June in the new premises of the Institution of Civil Engineers, 1–7 Great George Street. Dinner followed at 7.30 p.m. at Princes Restaurant. At the meeting a ballot was conducted for two new members, the successful candidates being Kenneth Alfred Wolfe Barry, the second son of Sir John, and Charles Langbridge Morgan, chief engineer of the London Brighton and South Coast Railway and Newhaven Harbour Co. Before the meeting closed, John Hutton Balfour Browne, KC, was elected President for 1915; he was a Bencher of the Middle Temple, and had been the Registrar and Secretary of the Railway Commission some years before.

The declaration of war on 4 August came in the recess of the Society's activities but immediately affected many of the members. At first there was optimism that the war would be over before Christmas, but by the end of the year hope of an early end to hostilities had faded. When the accounts were made up for the year ended 31 December 1914 there remained a balance in hand of £124 9s 4d, which was put on deposit to accrue interest. All activity ceased, and no subscriptions were collected during the war years.

It was not long after the Armistice of 11 November 1918 that the Society resumed its activities. A meeting of members was called for 6.30 p.m. on 29 January 1919 at Princes Restaurant. Sir Alexander Kennedy took the chair, and it was agreed that, notwithstanding the provisions of the Rules, this meeting would be considered a General Meeting. The Minutes of the previous Annual General Meeting held on 24 June 1914 were read, confirmed and signed by the Chairman. Balfour Browne, elected President for 1915, had not had the opportunity of presiding over the Society and so the Chairman proposed that he be the President for 1919 and he was re-elected.

As was to be expected after a lapse of four and a half years, the membership ranks had been severely depleted. There were twelve vacancies for ordinary members and one for an honorary member. It so happened that twelve candidates had been proposed and seconded and all were declared elected. Their number included William Vaux Graham, Ernest Frederic Crosbie Trench, Charles Pratt Sparks, John McFarlane Kennedy and Major Thomas Garmondsway Wrightson, the eldest son of Sir Thomas. In the ballot for an honorary member, Professor John Cunningham McLennan, physicist, was elected. The Chairman proposed that the Rules be examined to see whether any changes were needed, and if so, proposals for alterations could be brought to the next AGM. Proposals were circulated and discussed at the AGM held on 25 June 1919, and the alterations were adopted.

The President elected for 1920 was Saxton Noble, Sir Andrew's second son, who was the Managing Director of Sir W.G. Armstrong Whitworth & Co. Ltd. In 1891 he had married Celia Brunel James, the daughter of Isambard Kingdom Brunel's only daughter Florence, who had married Arthur James, an Eton housemaster.

The dinners in 1919 were held at Princes Restaurant, but then the venue was changed to the Hotel Jules, 85–86 Jermyn Street. From 1920 to 1923 the dinners were well attended and the June dinner each year was preceded by the AGM held in the Committee Room of the Institution of Civil Engineers.

At the AGM in 1920, the President, Saxton Noble was in the chair, and 15 members (including the Hon. Treasurer) attended. There were five candidates for two vacancies for ordinary members and two vacancies and five candidates for honorary membership. The ballot papers contained a reminder of Rule VII, namely, that no candidate shall be elected unless he obtains the votes of at least two–thirds of the members present.

As there were 16 members present on this occasion, 11 votes were the minimum required for election. The members elected were Sir John Purser Griffiths, the former Chief Engineer of the Dublin Port and Harbour Board, and Kenneth Hawksley, the son of Charles; the honorary members were Joseph Shaw, KC, and Sir Aston Webb, architect, President of the Royal Academy.

When the next AGM came round in June 1921, four vacancies for ordinary members were declared and there were six candidates, but no names had been put forward for the two vacancies for honorary members which had arisen. The members elected were Sir Eustace Tennyson D'Eyncourt, Director of Naval Construction, Admiralty; Sir John Snell, Chairman of the Electricity Commission; William Archer Porter Tait, former pupil and assistant to Sir John Wolfe

Charles Hawksley   *William Worthington*

Barry and Henry Marc Brunel; and Lieutenant Colonel James Carmichael, RE, of the Crown Agents for the Colonies.

The dinner on 29 June 1921 was a special event. In May the Secretary of the Institution of Civil Engineers had informed the President of the Society, John Strain, that twelve leading members of the American Engineering Societies would be visiting the Institution in order to present their John Fritz medal to Sir Robert Hadfield. The Society invited the American delegation to dinner.

Their leader was Charles F. Rand, Chairman of the Engineering Foundation, a body administered jointly by the American Society of Civil Engineers, American Institute of Mining and Metallurgical Engineers, American Society of Mechanical Engineers and the American Institute of Electrical Engineers. Afterwards the Chairman wrote "We shall never forget your very kind hospitality. Many sincere friendships were made that should have a lasting benefit".

In 1922 Sir John Biles was proposed for President, but he suggested that in view of his long membership John Rennie should take his turn; however, Rennie declined, saying that he felt it a sufficient honour to serve the Society as Hon. Treasurer, as he had done for the past 20 years, and he would continue to serve in that capacity if it was the wish of the members that he should do so. He was reassured by the members, who declared how much they valued his services as

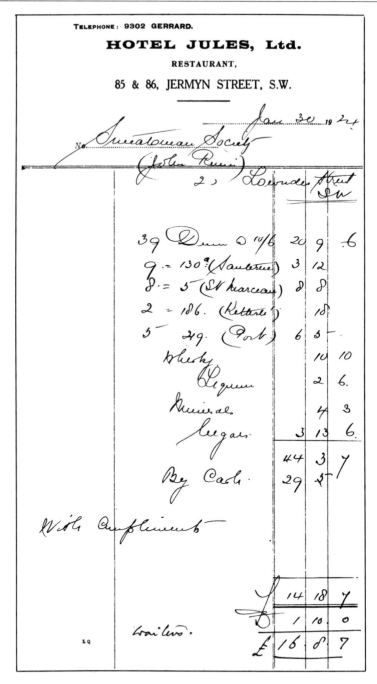

Dinner at Hotel Jules, 30 January 1924

Hon. Treasurer. Professor Sir John Biles, naval constructor and consultant was then elected President.

There was a vacancy for one ordinary member: only one candidate had been proposed but a ballot was deemed necessary, to ensure that at least two-thirds of the members present supported the candidate. William Wylie Grierson, Chief Engineer of the Great Western Railway was elected. Three candidates for honorary membership were also elected; the Duke of Northumberland, Sir Bruce Bruce-Porter, physician, and Viscount Dawson of Penn, the King's doctor, but Lord Dawson declined.

The suitability of the time-honoured title of "honorary member" was questioned at the AGM in 1923. It was thought by some to be inappropriate, because all members not only had the same rights and privileges, but paid the same subscription; "honorary members" it was said by some, should not be expected to pay the annual contribution. After much discussion it was decided that the conditions of honorary membership should not be changed. Three honorary members were then elected: Lord Ashfield, Chairman, London Passenger Transport Board; Sir Richard Threlfall, physicist and chemical engineer; and Sir George Beilby, the industrial chemist.

Sir Robert Elliott Cooper, the railway engineer, was the President in 1923, and he was followed by Sir Maurice Fitzmaurice, an ex-pupil of Sir Benjamin Baker. He worked for Baker and Sir John Fowler before entering the London County Council under Sir Alexander Binnie, whom he succeeded as Chief Engineer in 1901. He became a partner with Coode, Son and Matthews on his retirement from the LCC. He was elected President at the AGM in June 1923 and presided at the first dinner of the 1924 session on 30 January at the Hotel Jules, which was attended by 39 members and guests.

Illness prevented Sir Maurice attending the AGM on 25 June 1924, and Sir Robert Elliott Cooper took the chair. The dinner which followed the meeting was a celebration of the bicentenary of the birth of John Smeaton (8 June 1724 N.S.). The epitaph on the memorial to Smeaton in the Parish Church at Whitkirk was quoted: "A man whom God had endowed with the most extraordinary abilities, which he indefatigably exerted for the benefit of mankind in works of science and philosophical research, more especially as an engineer and mechanic".

A model of the base stones of the Eddystone Lighthouse, made in oak by Smeaton himself, was exhibited at the dinner; it showed how the lower layers of stone keyed together. The model was demonstrated by Colonel E. Kitson Clark, of the Airedale Foundry, Leeds (the guest of John Rennie), who later presented it to the Leeds City

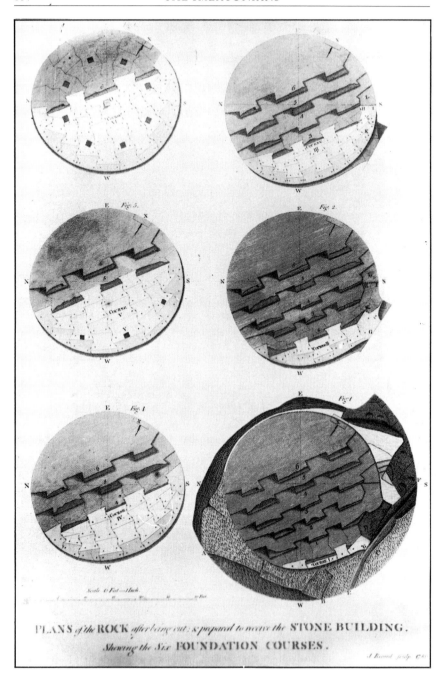

Model of foundations, Eddystone Lighthouse

Museum. Wooden models of other portions of the lighthouse, made for Smeaton by Josias Jessop, his general assistant, were in the possession of the Royal Scottish Museum, Edinburgh, the members were told. As a commentary on these exhibits, a copy of the second edition, 1813, of Smeaton's Eddystone Lighthouse Report was produced at the dinner, and extracts were read from it.

Tragically, Sir Maurice Fitzmaurice died before the end of the year. The President for 1925, elected at the AGM in June 1924, was Alan Archibald Campbell Swinton, of Edinburgh. On leaving Fettes College he entered a five year apprenticeship at the Elswick Works of Sir W.G. Armstrong & Co. In 1887 he went to London to practise as an electrical contractor and consultant, but gave up the contracting side in 1904. His hobby was photography and he produced the first X-ray photographs in 1896, only a month after Röntgen's discovery of X-rays. Thereafter his work was much in demand by the medical profession. His main work of electric power generation brought him into collaboration with the Hon. Charles Parsons on turbo-generator development.

The President was absent from the AGM on 25 June 1925, due to illness, and Professor Sir John Biles presided. There was a ballot to fill two vacancies for members, and David Hay, the partner of Basil Mott, and George William Humphreys, who had succeeded Sir Maurice Fitzmaurice as Chief Engineer of the London County Council in 1913, were the successful candidates out of a list of seven. Thirty-two members attended the meeting and it was after two ballots that the required two-thirds of votes were reached in both cases.

There were three candidates for honorary membership and all three were elected. They were Sir James Devonshire, Chairman, Northmet Power Co.; Rear Admiral Sir Douglas Brownrigg; and the Rt Hon. Hugh Pattison McMillan, KC, Lord Advocate of Scotland and a Privy Councillor.

The following year's President was Henry Reginald Arnulph Mallock. On leaving Oxford he had assisted his uncle, William Froude, at the Admiralty Ship Model Tank at Torquay, and then became an assistant to Lord Rayleigh. He was a scientist and also a skilled scientific instrument maker, with a wide range of interests. He was in the chair at the AGM on 26 June 1926. One ordinary member had resigned and two had died, so a ballot was held for three from a list of eight: 33 members were present, but only Sir John Thornycroft, Managing Director of John I. Thornycroft & Co. Ltd, received the required number of votes in the first ballot. In the second ballot Engineer Vice Admiral Sir Robert Dixon and Sir Brodie Henderson,

John Smeaton by George Romney

consulting engineer, were successful. In the only vacancy for an honorary member, Robert Reginald Johnston Turner, solicitor, was elected.

The question of absent members was raised by Frederick Palmer. Since so many people wished to join the Society but were unable to do so as membership numbers were limited, he suggested introducing a new rule to the effect that any member who was absent from the meetings without reasonable excuse should cease to be a member. This being the last meeting of the session, Palmer proposed to give notice of introducing a new Rule the following year, under the provisions of Rule XVI, but nothing came of this suggestion.

Before the meeting closed Dr Worthington proposed the election of John Rennie as President for the 1927 session; his proposal was seconded in writing by all the members of the Society; this time Rennie accepted nomination and was elected unanimously. He retained his post of Hon. Treasurer, and it was arranged that much of

Centenary of the Incorporation
by Royal Charter
of

The Institution of Civil Engineers

3 June, 1828.

The President and Council of The Institution of Civil Engineers extend a most cordial invitation to

The Smeatonian Society of Civil Engineers to be represented by a delegate at the celebration of the Centenary of the Incorporation of the Institution by Royal Charter, which will take place in the week beginning on the 3rd June, 1928.

The Institution was established on the 2nd January 1818 and was granted a Royal Charter on the 3rd June, 1828, "for the general advancement of Mechanical Science, and more particularly for promoting that species of knowledge which constitutes the profession of a Civil Engineer, being the art of directing the Great Sources of Power in Nature for the use and convenience of man."

Westminster, ~~August, 1927.~~
May 1928.

Centenary of the Royal Charter of the Institution of Civil Engineers the secretarial work would be undertaken by Hugh Biles, a lawyer, the nephew of Sir John. However, Biles had to withdraw in January due to illness and Rennie carried on the duties of both offices alone.

Through the initiative of Hugh Macmillan the Society was given the opportunity of acquiring the painting of John Smeaton by George Romney. A fund was opened for its purchase, and members were asked to subscribe £10 each towards the cost of £620. Only 40 members responded and the sum raised was not sufficient. When all seemed lost, Hugh Macmillan offered to make up the sum, and through his generosity the purchase was completed by Leggat Bros, the art dealers, in July 1926. The Institution of Civil Engineers accepted custody of the painting on behalf of the Society and agreed to assign a permanent place in the Institution's building, for it and for the other records and models of the Society, where they would be

The John Rennie Cup

available for inspection by the members and other interested persons. At the dinner which followed the AGM in 1930, each of the guests was given a framed reproduction of the painting.

Dr William Barton Worthington was elected President for 1928. After graduating at Owens College, Manchester, he was articled to his father, Samuel Worthington. In 1875 he joined Blyth and Cunningham, Edinburgh and was engaged in railway construction. He was appointed Engineer-in-Chief, Midland Railway, in 1905 and retired in 1915 to practise as a consulting engineer in London. The year 1928 was the centenary of the grant of the Royal Charter to the Institution of Civil Engineers and the President of the Society, Dr Worthington, and the Hon. Treasurer, John Rennie, attended the celebrations and presented an illuminated address to the President of the Institution, Ernest Crosbie Trench, on behalf of the members of the Society.

As the 1928 session drew to a close, the attention of members was drawn to the fact that John Rennie had served as Hon. Treasurer for 25 years. In moving a special vote of thanks to him, Frederick Palmer referred to the "Silver Wedding of John Rennie and the Smeatonian Society". The vote was carried with acclamation, and a silver cup was presented to Rennie, a gift from his fellow Smeatonians.

Engineer Vice Admiral Sir Henry Oram was the President for the following year. Starting as a student under the Chief Engineer, Devonport Dockyard, and then at the Royal Naval College, Greenwich, his career culminated in his appointment as Engineer-in-Chief of the Fleet in 1907, a post which he held until his retirement in 1917. The President in 1930 was Dr John Tudsbery Tudsbery, the Hon. Secretary of the Institution of Civil Engineers. He was a graduate of Glasgow University and obtained his doctorate there; then he became a pupil of George Deacon. He practised in Liverpool, before joining the staff of the Institution in 1892. He became the Secretary four years later and on his retirement in 1922 was made Honorary Secretary for life.

Chapter Seven

1931–1960

On Tuesday, 17 February 1931 a Special General Meeting was held at the Institution of Civil Engineers. It was the first such meeting to be held, although they had been introduced into the Rules in 1921. The President, Sir John Aspinall, consultant mechanical engineer to the Ministry of Transport and to the newly formed LMS Railway Co. presided. It was agreed that henceforth the admission of new members was not to be confined to the AGM in June.

The Hon. Sir Charles Parsons had died, Sir John Snell and Joseph Shaw, KC, had resigned. Three vacancies for ordinary members were filled by Sir Leopold Savile, Sydney Donkin and Sir Cyril Kirkpatrick; Sir Lynden Macassey, KC, was made an honorary member. Two more members were elected at the AGM in June, and Sir Archibald Denny became the President elect for 1932.

There was no provision in the rules of the Society for dealing with members in arrears of subscriptions and indeed there never had been. At the Hon. Treasurer's suggestion a committee was appointed to look into the matter. At the AGM in June 1932 an amendment to the Rules was proposed by Sir John Aspinall, seconded by Sir Archibald Denny, and approved. The revised rule read: "That an annual contribution, *payable in January*, the amount of which shall be determined each year by the Hon. Treasurer, shall be collected from all members of the Society, to defray the fixed and general expenses. *That the name of any member whose contribution is in arrears for the current and preceding year, shall, with the consent of the Annual General Meeting, be removed from the list of Members*".

An SGM was convened on 12 December, at the written request of five members, for the purpose of filling the vacancies caused by the deaths of three members. Sir Murdoch MacDonald, MP, the consulting engineer, was elected an ordinary member, and Sir Richard Gregory, the Professor of Astronomy, Queens College, London, and Henry Archibald Sandars, solicitor, became honorary members; but Sandars died before the next session.

Another SGM was called at the Hotel Jules on 25 January, prior to the first meeting of the 1933 session. It was called by the Hon. Treasurer because Sir Basil Mott, who had been elected President at the previous AGM, had intimated that he felt unable to take up the duty. Kenneth Wolfe Barry was then elected President. Educated at Winchester College and Trinity College, Cambridge, he had been articled to his father, whose practice he joined as a partner later. In 1902 he had married John Strain's daughter, Helen. At the AGM in June, another honorary member was elected in place of Sandars and Sir Charles Morgan was elected President for 1934. The vacancy for another ordinary member was filled at an SGM in January 1934.

The acquisitions of the Society had begun to grow once more. In 1934 Colonel E. Kitson Clark and Ernest Morgan presented documents and prints of interest to the Society; and Miss Jean Mylne, a great-granddaughter of William Chadwell Mylne, gave the Society reproductions of the engravings of William and his father Robert, which were in her possession.

At the meeting in May 1935 Sir Alexander Gibb produced a letter from the Secretary of the Society for the Protection of Ancient Buildings which stated that Austhorpe Lodge, Smeaton's birthplace and lifelong home, was in jeopardy. It had been bought by a developer who had already pulled down Smeaton's historic work-shop. The neighbourhood was gradually being engulfed by the suburbs of Leeds and although it was conceded that the house, built for John Smeaton's grand-father, had no great architectural merit, it was of great historical and sentimental interest to engineers, especially to the members of the Society. While expressing great interest it was clear that the Society did not have the resources to take any action.

The Corporation of Leeds was planning an exhibition devoted to the life of Smeaton and the Town Clerk enquired whether the Society would lend them the original Minute Book and the Romney portrait of Smeaton for their display. The loan of one of the facsimile Minute Books was approved, but not the original, and the painting was lent on condition that the Corporation paid the extra insurance premium involved and met all the expenses of packaging and transport.

The Society still held a few copies of the facsimile of the original Minute Book which had been produced in 1888, but renewed interest was being shown in it and the question of obtaining further reproductions was raised. An estimate was obtained; they could be produced for £1 each, if 100 copies were ordered. When the members were informed, only 29 expressed their interest, and they were told that they would have to pay £2 if the project were to go ahead. Eighty copies were ordered, and although this meant a higher cost, those who had already agreed to subscribe were allowed to take a copy for £2; the remainder were to be sold at £2 10s in order to recover the overall cost.

The election of new members took place at the meetings in June 1934 and in January and June 1935. At an SGM in January 1936 there were five candidates for two vacancies for ordinary members; only after the fourth ballot did two candidates secure the required two-thirds of the votes of those present.

The election procedure was running into difficulties, particularly because of the excessive number of ballots required before the provisions of the rules were met. The Presidents' Committee was convened to consider this and other matters. It was attended by the President Ernest Crosbie Trench, Sir Archibald Denny, Sir Basil Mott, Kenneth Wolfe Barry, Sir Charles Morgan, William Vaux Graham and the Hon. Treasurer, John Rennie.

The committee ruled out any reversion to the former practice of vetting the list of candidates and making a selection for the ballot list, as they considered this to be highly undesirable. Nevertheless they were firmly of the opinion that all branches of the engineering profession should be represented in the Society and a balance maintained. This, however, they felt would have to be left to the judgement of the members in the way they cast their votes. It would be helpful to the members, they thought, to have more time to consider the candidates proposed before the ballot took place, and this could be achieved by advancing the timetable for elections.

The committee recommended that any member wishing to propose a candidate for election should do so 21 days before the General Meeting, and that the ballot list should be sent to the members by the Hon. Treasurer not less than 14 days before the meeting. But the main recommendation of the committee was to make a significant change in the voting procedure. After the first ballot, those candidates who received the least number of votes should be eliminated, so as to leave two candidates for each vacancy. In the second ballot those receiving the greatest number of votes would be declared elected. Only in the case of a tie would another ballot be needed. The two-thirds rule was to be abandoned.

The Presidents' Committee was asked to consider other matters too. At the meeting in January 1936 William Binnie had drawn attention to what appeared to be a growing practice of canvassing in the matter of votes for election to membership, a practice he deplored, a view shared by many of the members. The members of the committee were unanimous in their views that such a practice was undesirable, but it was not a matter which could be dealt with by the

Austhorpe Lodge, Leeds

Rules. If the matter were to be brought before the members at the next General Meeting and the committee's view endorsed by a majority of the members, they felt sure the practice would cease.

The question of members who did not attend meetings was brought up again. It had been raised by Sir Frederick Palmer in 1926 without any action being taken then, but on finding that the number of members involved was small, the committee decided to make no recommendation. The recommendations of the committee were discussed at the AGM on 27 May 1936, and were adopted. The Rules which affected the ballot were amended.

John Rennie suggested to the committee that the time had come for him to be relieved of much of the responsibility for the secretarial work. Part of his time was now spent in the country and the facilities available to him in London were no longer what they used to be, so he suggested it was time to get a younger man to act as Secretary. He was quite willing to remain as Hon. Treasurer, in which capacity he had served for 33 years, if he could shed some of the secretarial work. There had never been a Secretary, so if one were appointed it would be a new post. Several names were mentioned and Rennie promised to consider what was said and report back.

The John Rennie Memorial

The committee met again on 30 April, and expressed their opinion that whoever was to take on the job of Secretary must have a residence and office in London. There were many questions which arose from time to time, which required immediate attention which could best be dealt with by the Secretary if he was on the spot. The committee's next meeting was on 3 November when Charles Sparks, the President-elect for 1937, joined it. The post of Secretary was approved and John Garmondsway Wrightson, the eldest son of Sir Guy, although not himself a member, was invited to undertake it. He was introduced to the committee and appointed with effect from 1 December. The committee expressed the hope that Miss Elizabeth Bickell, who had done much of the secretarial work in the past, would continue to assist, and asked that she be specifically requested to do so. John Rennie would continue to be the Hon. Treasurer.

In 1921 there was a proposal to erect a monument to John Rennie (1761–1821) at East Linton, close to his birthplace, where he had served his apprenticeship. The Society was asked for support, and a contribution of £25 was sent, accompanied by a request to the architect for photographs of the memorial for each member.

There was no lack of interest in the history of the Society although little had been written except for Sir John Rennie's unpublished attempt in 1873 and George Banks Rennie's pamphlet in 1888. In 1937 Sydney Donkin read a paper about the Smeatonians, at a meeting of the Newcomen Society which had been founded in 1920 to study the history of engineering and technology. He sought permission to publish it which was granted, with a proviso that he would make copies available to any interested members and present a copy to the Society for its archives.

The Hon. Secretary wrote to the President of the Institution of Civil Engineers, Sir Alexander Gibb, in February 1937, asking whether the Institution would house the books, pictures and other items which the Society had acquired. The Institution already accommodated the portrait of Smeaton and other documents, and it was thought that, if a permanent home was available, other items of interest might be forthcoming. The Council of the Institution acceded to this request and a number of items were handed over to the Secretary of the Institution on 23 June. These included the old mahogany box marked "Society of Civil Engineers" on a brass plate, a folio copy of Smeaton's Eddystone Lighthouse report, the four quarto volumes of Smeaton's works, one copy of the old edition of the facsimile Minute Book of 1771, and two copies of the latest reprint, a copy of the "Toasts and Sentiment", and two silver trowels which commemorated the laying of bridge foundation stones.

On going through some papers belonging to his late father, the Hon. Treasurer reported finding the Minute Books which followed on from the original one, also the members' signature book, and these were handed over to the Institution too.

Six more books were sent to the Institution on 15 July, including a fair copy of the Minutes and Accounts 1771–1807 which George Rennie had made, three volumes of the Treasurer's Minutes and Accounts covering the periods 1793–1821, 1822–1882 and 1883–1902, the attendance book 1876–1912 and the Lists of Members 1812–1927. In his covering letter the Hon. Secretary stressed the very great interest of these documents and asked that no one should have access to them without written authority. It was left to the President of the Society, Sir John Kennedy, and the Secretary to decide upon the wording to be placed over the bookcase containing the Society's possessions in the Institution's library.

There were five vacancies for ordinary members caused by five deaths during 1936 and five candidates at the SGM in January 1937; all were elected by a show of hands, there being no need for a ballot. At the AGM in June there were four vacancies for which ten candidates had been proposed and seconded. Under the new voting procedure two ballots sufficed. Vacancies for one ordinary member and one honorary member were filled at the AGM in June 1938; and in March 1939 an SGM was convened for the purpose of electing two members from a list of nine nominees and two honorary members from three. The first ballot reduced the nine candidates to four and the second ballot produced the two new ordinary members. The two honorary members were elected in one ballot. The new election procedure was said to be working well.

During the 1937 session dinners took place at the Hotel Jules for the last time; in 1938 they were held at the Athenaeum, by kind permission of the Chairman and Committee of the Club. These arrangements were renewed in 1939. However, when in the early part of 1939 plans were being made for the 1940 session, the Athenaeum indicated that they were not prepared to continue the arrangement and another venue had to be found. A strong preference was expressed for holding the dinners on private premises, and the Secretary in consultation with the Hon. Treasurer and the Presidents' Committee was charged with finding a satisfactory location.

Sir Guy Wrightson succeeded Sir John Kennedy as President in 1939. Having joined the Society in 1919 as Major Thomas Wrightson, he had taken the title of Sir Guy Wrightson on succeeding to the baronetcy in 1921. During the 1939 session, a meeting of the Society received publicity in the press. At the AGM in June, the President expressed his concern at this, reminding the members that such reports were not allowed and were particularly objectionable when the dinners were held in private premises; members were expected to be aware of this, but were asked to make it clear to their guests that such reports were not permitted.

John Smeaton had divided his time between Leeds and London. His home and office were at Austhorpe Lodge, Leeds; he took lodgings when in London until in 1783 he moved to chambers at Gray's Inn which he leased for the rest of his life, spending the parliamentary session, January to June, there except when visiting the sites of his work. The Newcomen Society in 1939 proposed to place a commemorative plaque on the building in Gray's Inn which Smeaton had occupied and the Smeatonian Society agreed to bear half the cost.

War broke out in September 1939 in the recess in the Society's activities. Captain John Wrightson, the Secretary, had been called up for active service, and John Rennie once again combined the duties of Secretary with those of Hon. Treasurer. The original Minute Book, which the Society had retained, and important records were deposited in the strongroom of the Westminster Bank; the painting and other valuables were in the care of the Institution. No meetings were held in 1940; subscriptions were waived and the funds of the Society invested partly in a Post Office Savings Account and partly on deposit at the bank.

In March 1941, Rennie arranged a luncheon at the Junior Carlton Club, Pall Mall, which was attended by 20 members and 14 guests. A second lunchtime meeting was held in October, and this was declared a General Meeting for the conduct of business. The Hon. Treasurer enquired whether members wished to hold further lunches in 1942. If so, he suggested a reduced subscription of one guinea be paid in addition to the cost of the lunches. It was decided to hold three luncheons between January and June, the traditional session.

Between the AGM in June 1939 and October 1941 the Society had lost 15 members: thirteen had died and two resigned. With such a regrettably large number of vacancies it was clear that the choice of new members would be much less competitive than usual and it was proposed that the number to be elected be restricted. After discussion, the Rules were amended by adding the words *"not more than six members of the First Class of Membership shall be elected at any meeting"*. Six first class members were then elected from 17 candidates by the balloting process and one honorary member by a show of hands. The description of the engineer as First Class Member had been dropped in 1827; now it was resumed in the affairs of the Society but it did not reappear in the list of Members until 1971. Sir

LIST OF THE MEMBERS

Date of
Election

JANUARY, 1939.

1900	SIR SAXTON WILLIAM ARMSTRONG NOBLE, Bt. – –	Kent House, Knightsbridge, S.W.7.
1901	JOHN A RENNIE – – – – – – –	Bishops Green House, Newbury, Berks.
1904	SIR R. ELLIOTT-COOPER, K.C.B. – – – – – –	44, Princes Gate, S.W.7.
,,	SIR R. A. HADFIELD, Bt., D.Sc., D.Met., F.R.S. – –	22, Carlton House Terrace, S.W.1.
1909	Engineer VICE-ADMIRAL SIR HENRY ORAM, K.C.B., F.R.S. –	Kilmory, Cranleigh, Surrey.
1914	SIR CHARLES L. MORGAN, C.B.E. – – – – –	Hotel Rubens, Buckingham Palace Road, S.W.1.
1919	WILLIAM VAUX GRAHAM, M.Inst.C.E. – – – –	5, Queen Anne's Gate, S.W.1.
,,	ERNEST FREDERIC CROSBIE TRENCH, M.A., B.A.I. –	Stokke Manor, Great Bedwyn, Wilts.
,,	CHARLES PRATT SPARKS, C.B.E., M.Inst.C.E., M.I.E.E. –	6, Wellesley Court, West Parade, Worthing, Sussex.
,,	JOHN McFARLANE KENNEDY – – – – –	Electricity Commission, Savoy Court, Strand, W.C.2.
,,	SIR GUY WRIGHTSON, Bt. – – – – –	Neasham Hall, Nr. Darlington.
1921	SIR EUSTACE TENNYSON D'EYNCOURT, Bt., K.C.B. R.C.N.C., F.R.S., LL.D, D.Sc., M.Inst.C.E. –	20, Ebury Street, S.W.1.
1924	SIR WESTCOTT STILE ABELL, K.B.E., M.Eng. – –	12, Westfield Drive, Gosforth, Newcastle-on-Tyne.
,,	BRIG. GEN. SIR HENRY PERCY MAYBURY, G.B.E., K.C.M.G., C.B., M.Inst.C.E., J.P. – – – – – –	Bush House, Aldwych, London, W.C.2.
,,	MAURICE FITZGERALD WILSON, M.Inst.C.E. – –	11, The Grove, Boltons, London, S.W.7.
1925	SIR GEORGE WILLIAM HUMPHREYS, K.B.E., M.Inst.C.E. –	10, Victoria Street, S.W.1.
1926	Engineer VICE-ADMIRAL SIR ROBERT DIXON, K.C.B. –	Queen Anne's Mansions, St. James' Park, S.W.1.
,,	SIR JOHN E. THORNYCROFT, K.B.E. – – –	Old Ferry House, 5, Chelsea Embankment, S.W.
1927	SIR RICHARD AUGUSTINE STUDDERT REDMAYNE, K.C.B. –	34, Victoria Street, Westminster, S.W
,,	W. J. E. BINNIE, M.A., M.Inst.C.E. – – – –	Artillery House, Artillery Row, Victoria Street, S.W.1.
1928	E. W. MONKHOUSE, M.V.O., M.A. – – – –	14, Old Queen Street, Westminster, S.W.
1929	SIR CLEMENT DANIEL MAGGS HINDLEY, K.C.I.E., M.A.	High Elms, The Green, Hampton Court.
,,	SIR ALEXANDER GIBB, G.B.E., C.B., LL.D.(Edin.), F.R.S.	Queen Anne's Lodge, Westminster, S.W.
1931	SIR LEOPOLD H. SAVILE, K.C.B., M.Inst.C.E. –	23, Pelham Crescent, S.W.7.
,,	SIDNEY BRYAN DONKIN – – – – –	Broadway Court, 8, Broadway, Westminster, S.W.
,,	SIR CYRIL KIRKPATRICK, M.Inst.C.E. – – –	Loudhams, Amersham, Bucks.
,,	CHARLES GEORGE DU CANE, O.B.E., M.Inst.C.E. –	164, Grosvenor Gardens House, Grosvenor Gardens, S.W
1932	Engineer VICE-ADMIRAL SIR R. W. SKELTON, K.C.B., C.B.E., D.S.O. – – – – – –	Meadow Cottage, Aldingbourne, Chichester.
,,	SIR ARTHUR HENRY PREECE, M.Inst.C.E. – –	8, Queen Anne's Gate, Westminster, S.W.1.
,,	SIR HERBERT NIGEL GRESLEY, C.B.E., D.Sc., M.Inst C.E.	Watton House, Hertford.
,,	SIR MURDOCH MacDONALD, K.C.M.G., C.B., M.Inst.C.E., M.P. –	72, Victoria Street, Westminster, S.W.1.
1934	DAVID ANDERSON, B.Sc., LL.D. – – – –	9, Iddesleigh House, Westminster, S.W.1.
,,	RUSTAT BLAKE, M.A., M.Inst.C.E., M.I.Mech.E., M.I.E.Aust.	Queen Anne's Lodge, Westminster, S.W.1.
1935	W. T. HALCROW, M.Inst.C.E. – – – –	16, Victoria Street, Westminster, S.W.1.
,,	GERALD W. PARTRIDGE, M.Inst.C.E. – –	13, Langland Gardens, Hampstead, N.W.
1936	Engineer VICE-ADMIRAL SIR HAROLD BROWN, K.C.B.	3, Albert Place, W.8.
1937	ARTHUR TREVENEN COODE, M.Inst.C.E. – – –	9, Victoria Street, Westminster, S.W.
,,	T. PEIRSON FRANK, M.Inst.C.E., F.S.I. – – –	Chief Engineer's Department, The County Hall, Westminster Bridge, S.E.1.
,,	HAROLD J. F. GOURLEY, M.Eng.(Liverpool), M.Inst.C.E. –	Artillery House, Artillery Row, Victoria Street, S.W.1.
,,	COLONEL DAVID LYELL, C.M.G., C.B.E., D.S.O., M.Inst.C.E.	7, Harrowby Court, Seymour Place, W.1.
,,	M. T. TUDSBERY, M.Inst.C.E. – – – –	Broadcasting House, W.1.
,,	ATHOL L. ANDERSON, C.B., M.Inst.C.E. – –	The Admiralty, Whitehall, S.W.
,,	R. CARPMAEL, O.B.E. – – – – –	Chief Engineer's Office, Paddington Station, W.2.
,,	LIEUT.-COLONEL J. R. DAVIDSON, C.M.G., M.Sc., M.Inst.C.E.	Metropolitan Water Board, Chief Engineer's Dept., 173, Rosebery Avenue, E.C.4.
,,	MAJOR F. C. COOK, C.B., D.S.O., M.C., M.Inst.C.E. –	Heene Croft, Oakfield Road, Ashtead, Surrey.
1938	JOHN D. WATSON, M.Inst.C.E. – – – –	Bella Vista, Northfield, Birmingham.

46

Honorary Members.

1922	SIR BRUCE BRUCE-PORTER, K.B.E., C.M.G., D.L., M.D. – –	
1923	THE RIGHT HON. LORD ASHFIELD, P.C. – – –	55, Broadway, Westminster, S.W.1.
1925	SIR JAMES L. DEVONSHIRE, K.B.E., M.I.E.E. – – –	Wall House, The Green, Wimbledon Common, S.W.19.
..	THE RIGHT HON. LORD MACMILLAN OF ABERFELDY, P.C., G.C.V.O., LL.D., Hon. M.Inst.C.E. –	44, Millbank, Westminster, S.W.1.
1926	ROBERT R. J. TURNER, O.B.E. – – – –	13, Evelyn Gardens, S.W.7.
1927	SIR HERBERT WALKER, K.C.B. – – – –	9, Maresfield Gardens, N.W.3.
1929	SIR WILLIAM BRAGG, O.M., K.B.E., LL.D., D.Sc., F.R.S. –	The Royal Institution, 21, Albemarle Street, W.1.
1932	CHARLES E. C. BROWNE – – – – –	15, Great College Street, Westminster, S.W.1.
1933	COLONEL SIR E. G. H COX, C.B.E., D.L. – –	23, Edwardes Square, Kensington, W.8.
1938	HON. MR. JUSTICE LANGTON – – – –	51, Draycott Place, S.W.

List of members, 1939

Westcott Abell, the Professor of Naval Architecture at Newcastle-upon-Tyne, who had been elected President for the 1940 session and had continued in office in 1941, handed over to Sir Eustace Tennyson D'Eyncourt, a director of Armstrong Whitworth & Co. Ltd and of Parsons Steam Turbine Co. Ltd, former Director of Naval Construction, Admiralty, who was elected President for 1942.

The AGM in 1942 was held at the Waldorf Hotel, Aldwych, on 15 July. There were 13 nominations for six vacancies for first class members, and following the regular procedure two ballots reduced the list to the required number. Brig. General Sir Henry Maybury, the former Director General of Roads, Ministry of Transport, was elected President for the coming session but sadly he died on 7 January 1943, and at the luncheon on 24 February Maurice Fitzgerald Wilson was elected for the remainder of the session. The three lunches held at the Waldorf Hotel during 1943 were well attended, averaging 45 members and guests. There had been an increase in the cost of lunch, although subject to government food restrictions, but the Society had ample funds and no increase in subscriptions was suggested.

Sir George Humphreys, the former Chief Engineer and Surveyor of the LCC and a practising consulting engineer was elected President for 1944, but he was absent from the luncheon held on 27 January and the Hon. Treasurer announced that Sir George had felt obliged to resign due to ill health. The meeting was declared an SGM for the purpose of choosing a new President and Sir John Thornycroft was elected. Sir George Humphreys died on 9 March 1945.

All three meetings during 1945 were luncheons, although the Hon. Treasurer had tried in vain to arrange a dinner for the last which coincided with the AGM. Everyone hoped that dinners could be resumed in 1946, the war being over, and that monthly meetings from January to June could be restored. There were two vacancies for first class members and two for honorary members in 1945, but before the ballots took place the President, Sir Richard Redmayne, the mining engineer, reminded members of the objections to canvassing for votes which had been expressed in 1936 and asked the members present if, in their opinion, canvassing for candidates before an election was still undesirable. The members unanimously agreed. Sir Richard then stated that canvassing had taken place, and so he had taken the opportunity to remind members of what had been decided in earlier times. By drawing attention to it he hoped it would cease. Before the meeting closed a very special vote of thanks was accorded to John Rennie for the admirable way he had carried on the business of the Society during the war years.

During 1946 there were four meetings, all of them dinners. John
Wrightson was back in harness in time for the AGM on 27 June, but
the Hon. Treasurer was unable to be present. Advantage was taken of
Rennie's absence to discuss a presentation to him, and the Secretary
was asked to obtain the views of Mr and Mrs Rennie as to the form it
should take and then to collect subscriptions for it from the members.
Both the President, Sir Alexander Gibb, and the Secretary were
absent from the AGM on 25 June 1947 and Ernest Crosbie Trench
took the chair. The reduction in the charge for dinner from £1 to 10s
for members, coupled with the resumption of six dinners during the
session, had reduced the balance of funds in hand. Nevertheless the
subscriptions were kept at £2 10s 0d for 1948. Rennie pointed out that
the subscription remained the same as before the war and added "we
are getting the same treatment as before the war except that we now
drink Hock instead of Champagne". The subscription remained the
same but dinner charges were increased to £1 for members and 25s for
a guest in 1949.

The notice of the AGM in 1947 disclosed two vacancies for first
class members, the number obtaining 21 days before the meeting, but
Sir John Kennedy had tendered his resignation after the notices had
gone out. Rule VII was waived in the circumstances and three new
members were elected from six candidates. John Wrightson, the
Secretary, was one of the successful ones. Sir Athol Anderson asked if
a luncheon could be arranged during the coming session as this would
be more convenient than a dinner for those living out of London. It
was agreed to hold a luncheon, but in addition to the usual dinners:
November or December was suggested as the appropriate time.

The question of again wearing evening dress at dinner was
discussed but it was agreed that this should remain optional for the
time being. Before the meeting closed a vote of thanks was passed to
the Chairman, Committee, Secretary and Staff of the Junior Carlton
Club, for enabling the Society to hold its dinners there. Thanks were
also expressed to Miss Elizabeth Bickell, who had tendered her
resignation after 30 years of valuable service to the Society, doing the
secretarial work ever since taking over from J. Perry in John Rennie's
office.

When Sydney Bryan Donkin was elected President in 1949 his
family had been represented in the membership from 1835, when his
great-grandfather, Bryan Donkin (1768–1855) joined; a record which
has only been surpassed by the Mylnes and the Rennie family.

John Assheton Rennie, the Hon. Treasurer, died on 15 February
1949 and at the dinner on 23 February the President paid a glowing
tribute to him.

The Presidents' Committee was convened in April to choose Rennie's successor. They recommended the nomination of John Wrightson for election at the next AGM as Hon. Treasurer.

Mrs Rennie's offer of the cup presented to her husband in 1928 was warmly received; it was accepted as a memorial to him, to be placed with the Society's other possessions in the care of the Institution of Civil Engineers and to "grace the table" at the Society's dinners.

The question of honorary members being expected to pay the annual subscription was raised again in the light of renewed criticism. The Hon. Treasurer pointed out that if their subscriptions were given up, the £30 per annum lost would have to be made good by an increase in the first class member's subscriptions. So as not to mislead proposed honorary members, the possibility of changing the title from "honorary" to "associate" member was discussed. There was a conflict of opinion in the committee; Sir John Thornycroft and Sydney Donkin both felt it inappropriate that honorary members should be asked to pay a subscription as they did not join the Society for any advantage available to them. Ernest Crosbie Trench and Sir Westcott Abell opposed this, and drew attention to the Rule which required the annual contribution to be collected from all the members. No agreement could be reached, so the matter was left open for general discussion at the AGM.

At that meeting it was explained that the question had arisen from letters the Hon. Treasurer had received from two gentlemen who did not think they should be called upon to pay, being honorary members, but another honorary member had written to the President pointing out that honorary members enjoyed the same privileges as first class members, which included the right to bring guests to dinner, to vote at elections for first class members as well as for honorary members and that therefore they should contribute to the funds on the same basis as first class members. When put to the vote it was decided that honorary members should continue to pay the annual subscription, and that the title "honorary member" should not be changed. Winding up the debate the President said that however eminent those proposed as honorary members might be, they should be persons considered congenial and suitable to be members of the Society by those proposing and seconding them. The Hon. Treasurer was asked to include in his circular letter calling for nominations a statement that those proposed as honorary members should be given to understand that being equally privileged as first class members, they would be called upon to pay the annual subscription.

The new ballot procedure had been used successfully for some time, but it was not free from problems. There were three candidates for one vacancy for a first class member in 1949. The purpose of the first ballot was to eliminate the candidate with the least votes. Vice-Admiral (E) Sir Denys Ford received most votes, but the votes of the other two were equal. Voting in the second ballot to eliminate one of them was 12 and 10. The third ballot was between Sir Denys and the survivor of the second ballot, but the votes were equal, 11 each. The President ruled that Sir Denys was elected, as he had the greatest number of votes in the first ballot. The validity of this ruling was questioned by one of the members and the matter was referred to the Presidents' Committee. After examining the three ballots fully, the committee endorsed the President's interpretation of the Rules. At the SGM on 25 January 1950, when Sir Cyril Kirkpatrick took the chair as President, there were vacancies for two first class members and three honorary members, one of the vacancies having been caused by the death of Sir Guy Wrightson on 7 January.

The Newcomen Society had undertaken to clean and repaint the memorial to Smeaton in the chancel of the Parish Church at Whitkirk, and their Secretary sought the Smeatonian Society's aid. It was agreed that the two societies would share the cost. Members were also told that the Newcomen Society was publishing "*A Catalogue of the Civil and Mechanical Engineering Designs 1714–92 of John Smeaton*". It listed papers which were preserved in the library of the Royal Society. Copies were available to members at 15*s* each and a copy was obtained for the records of the Society.

The next President was Engineer Vice Admiral Sir Reginald Skelton, who as Chief Engineer of the *Discovery* had accompanied Captain Scott to the Antarctic in 1901–04. He was the Engineer-in-Chief of the Fleet when he was elected a member in 1932, and after retirement from the Royal Navy had been made a director of John I. Thornycroft & Co. Ltd. He was followed in 1952 by Sir Murdoch MacDonald, the consulting engineer and MP for Invernesshire. There were only five meetings in 1952, the February meeting having been cancelled when it was learned that the King had died on 6 February.

At the April meeting the Romney portrait of Smeaton was on show, having been received back from Leggat Bros who had been asked to report on its condition. Their report describing its condition as excellent was received in time to be reported at the AGM in June. In 1955 the picture was moved from its usual place in the library of the Institution to the Junior Carlton Club, where it was to hang in the anteroom to the library to be on view to members of the Society and their guests attending the dinners.

At an SGM held on 28 January 1953 Sir John Thornycroft took the chair in the absence, through illness, of the President. It was

Sir Alexander Gibb   *Sir William Halcrow*

announced that HRH Prince Philip, Duke of Edinburgh, had consented to his name going forward for honorary membership. The great pleasure which his acceptance gave to members, and the honour which it conferred upon the Society, were conveyed to His Royal Highness in a letter, accompanied by a copy of the facsimile Minute Book, which also expressed the hope that he would dine with the members of the Society whenever possible. It was unanimously agreed not to call upon His Royal Highness to pay the annual subscription.

Miss Bonner, who had been conducting the secretarial work of the Society from the time of Miss Bickell's resignation in 1947 tendered her resignation in 1953, on the occasion of her marriage. The members gave her a wedding present of a coffee service. Miss Margaret Folliard took over the secretarial work.

At the June meeting Sir William Halcrow informed the members that the President, Sir David Anderson, had died on 27 March. Sir John Thornycroft proposed Sir William for President, and he was duly elected.

It had been the practice for many years for the outgoing President to nominate his successor and it had become the custom for him to name the next senior member by date of joining the Society, if he consented. When Sir William Halcrow, who had joined in 1935, proposed to nominate Engineer Vice Admiral Sir Harold Brown, who was elected in 1936, Sir Harold declined. Four members had been elected in 1937 and Sir William said he regarded their claims as equal. He proposed Sir Jonathan Davidson as President and he was elected. The same problem arose the following year when from two candidates with equal claims, the President decided the issue "in the way that Captains of opposing teams generally decided and he had done it in complete secrecy and as a result proposed Mr Tudsbery as President for the ensuing year".

Robert Turner died in 1955 and, announcing his death, the Hon. Treasurer referred to talks he had had with him following a suggestion made by several members that there should be someone to deputise for the Hon. Treasurer when he was unable to attend meetings. He had enquired of Robert Turner whether his son, Cecil, would be willing to act. Subsequently, the Hon. Treasurer said, he had been in correspondence with young Mr Turner who was willing and keen to act as Assistant Hon. Treasurer, as he was very interested in the history and traditions of the Society. Cecil Turner was introduced to the members at the dinner on 25 January and attended the AGM on 27 June 1956 in his official capacity as Assistant Hon. Treasurer. Three years later at a meeting when Marmaduke Tudsbery was in the chair he proposed that as soon as a vacancy occurred among the honorary members, serious thought should be given to seeing Cecil Turner "made an honest man". He was elected at the SGM on 23 March 1960.

Membership lists were up-dated and issued annually as they had been since 1883; to improve their presentation Colonel Charles Norrie proposed that Institution designations be omitted, and that only honours and awards, Fellowship of the Royal Society and academic qualifications be included. This met with general approval, and members were asked to indicate the initials that should properly appear after their names.

There were three vacancies for first class members in 1956, and six candidates. The three candidates elected were severally partners in three well-known and respected consulting engineering practices; the three unsuccessful candidates were a naval engineer officer, a professional civil servant and a director of a firm of civil engineering contractors.

Sir John Thornycroft wondered whether the Rules laid down for the election of new members were adequate. The names of certain eminent engineers had been put forward more than once, he said, but they had not been elected. It had always been the practice to have as broad a selection of first class members as possible, so that every facet of engineering could be represented in the Society. Responsibility rested with each member of the Society individually, and it should be appreciated that if the election of first class members were confined to one branch of the profession and denied to eminent men in other branches, the nature of the Society would change.

After the meeting Sir John sent a letter to the Hon. Treasurer clarifying his views and with the approval of the President, copies were sent to all the members. He explained that his concern arose from the repeated failure of the Engineer-in-Chief of the Fleet and the Director of Naval Construction to be elected. "They both hold positions of great responsibility and are highly regarded, as were their predecessors many of whom have been Members of the Society and added lustre to it" he stated. He would be reluctant to see their names put forward again without some certainty of their election, and he wondered if the members would be willing to elect them unanimously if vacancies were provided by the retirement of two members who had passed through the Chair. He would be pleased to be one and thought one of the other Past Presidents would also be willing to retire in these circumstances.

An SGM was convened on 30 January 1957 to discuss Sir John's letter. The Hon. Treasurer pointed out that the Society was the oldest society of non-military engineers in Britain, and when the Society was formed there were only two branches, civil and military. If the traditional character of the Society was to be maintained, members must be chosen from every facet of the engineering world and this must continue. He was against altering the Rules; the best way of solving the problem would be to leave it to individual members so to exercise their votes so that members from any one side of engineering would not dominate the Society. Several members who could not be present had written to the Hon. Treasurer and he quoted from their letters. Many members contributed to the discussion. The Chairman then summed up. All were grateful to Sir John, he said, for raising the matter and for his generous offer to resign to provide a vacancy, but it was the unanimous view of the members that this should not happen. The feeling was that, before the next election took place, the Hon. Treasurer should inform the members of the state of the Society at that time and say what the proportions had been in the various departments of engineering in the past. This was agreed and it was confirmed that no changes in the Rules would be made.

The Hon. Treasurer said it had been the practice over the past 20 years or so to limit the election of first class members to no more than four at any one time. If there were a large influx the balance could alter; he already had four offers of resignation and there had been two deaths; he asked for confirmation that only four vacancies should be filled and this was agreed. On 27 March 1957 a ballot was held for four vacancies for first class members, arising from the deaths of Engineer Vice Admiral Sir Reginald Skelton and Harold Gourley, and the resignation of Engineer Vice Admiral Sir Harold Brown and Sir Harold Yarrow. From a list of five candidates, those elected were Sir Claud Gibb, Chairman of C. A. Parsons & Co. and A Reynolle & Co. Ltd, Vice Admiral (E) Sir Frank Mason, Engineer-in-Chief of the Fleet, Sir Victor Shepheard, Director of Naval Construction, Admiralty and Robert Wynne-Edwards, Managing Director of Costain-John Brown Ltd. There were three vacancies to be filled in January 1958, and the successful candidates were Sir Christopher Hinton, Chairman, Central Electricity Generating Board, George Ambler Wilson, Chief Engineer, Port of London Authority, and Sir Harold Bishop, Director of Engineering, British Broadcasting Corporation.

When Thomas Hawksley came to the end of his year in office as President in 1958, Sir William Halcrow, proposing a vote of thanks to him, drew attention to the remarkable achievements of the Hawksley family. Thomas Hawksley (1807–1898) was a guest at the centenary dinner of the Society on 29 March 1871, and he was elected a member in 1872. Since then four generations of the family had been members and three of them had become Presidents, a truly notable record.

The balance of funds in hand had decreased by the end of the 1957 session. Expenditure on the dinners was considerably higher than previously; stationary and postage had gone up. There was money in the Post Office Savings Bank and the policy was not to build up a big balance, but the Hon. Treasurer felt it imprudent to draw heavily on the savings account because in a few years' time the Society might be faced with the expense of reprinting the facsimile Minute Book. Income could be raised by increasing the annual subscription, which had remained the same for 30 years, or by increasing the charge for dinners. The price of dinners was raised from 25s to 35s for members, and from 30s to £2 for guests. This increased the revenue by more than £100 in the next session, giving the Assistant Hon. Treasurer more leeway in making arrangements with the Junior Carlton Club for the dinners.

The first estimate for reprinting the facsimile Minute Book was £488 for 100 copies, which was thought to be excessive. Alternative quotations were sought: and these were £480 and £700 respectively. Reproduction by a photographic process was then suggested, for which the same firms quoted £250 and £290. An order was placed for 150 copies at a cost of £300, and members were asked to put up the

money. The members subscribed £294 17s and the Assistant Hon.
Treasurer negotiated a discount which kept the cost within the
money subscribed. The 1937 reprinting of the book had cost £100 15s
for 80 copies which had been sold for £2 and £2 10s; the new edition
would be sold for three guineas and the transactions kept in a separate
account.

Vice Admiral Sir Denys Ford suggested that it was time for a fund
to be set up, and built up over a period of years, to finance the
celebration of the 200th anniversary of the founding of the Society.
When the matter was raised at the AGM in June, the Hon. Treasurer
indicated that an increase of 10s in the annual subscription over the
next 10 years would produce approximately £300. This increase was
agreed and the Duo-Centenary Fund was started to collect both the
increase in subscriptions and the proceeds of sale of the facsimile
Minute Books.

Chapter Eight

1961–1988

For several years the General Meetings had been held at Ship House, 20 Buckingham Gate, the London offices of Head, Wrightson & Co. Ltd, but in 1961 they were held once more in the Council Room of the Institution of Civil Engineers; the dinners continued to take place at the Junior Carlton Club. The question of reserving seats at dinner was raised by Professor Pippard, who asked for blank cards to be provided on which a member could put his name and similarly the name of his guest, so that they could be seated appropriately. This was agreed and only on special occasions was a seating plan to be prepared in advance.

At the AGM in 1963, the Hon. Treasurer warned members that the Junior Carlton Club was about to be demolished and rebuilt; the Club's temporary home would be the Army and Navy Club, where the Society could continue to be offered hospitality if the members so wished, an offer the Society gladly accepted.

During the summer recess in 1965 a joint meeting with the Royal Society Dining Club was proposed. The suggestion came from HRH Prince Philip and was passed to the Presidents' Committee. The President, Sir George McNaughton, the Hon. Treasurer and the Assistant Hon. Treasurer met the officers of the Royal Society and made the arrangements. The joint dinner was held at Buckingham Palace in November 1966, when Prince Philip presided. Sadly, Sir George died before the event, and his successor, Vice Admiral Sir Denys Ford, who had been elected at the June AGM as President for the 1967 session, took over.

The rebuilding of the Junior Carlton Club was expected to complete in January 1967 and the Society was informed that when the Club re-occupied its premises, the Army and Navy Club would not be prepared to continue accommodating the Society's dinners. The Assistant Hon. Treasurer undertook to explore alternative accommodation, in case a complete change of venue was preferred. Dinners at the Army and Navy Club during 1966 had cost 52s per head. If the dinners in February and March 1967 were to be held at the United Service Club, the charge was expected to be more. No indication could be given of the charges to be made at the new Junior Carlton Club where the Society hoped to dine in April.

An increase in the members' contributions to the cost of dinner seemed inevitable, and the Hon. Treasurer was given authority to raise the charge, if and when necessary. As it turned out the Junior Carlton Club was not completed in time. Dinners continued to be held at the Army and Navy Club throughout 1967 and reservations were made there for 1968.

Sir John Wrightson suggested that it was not too soon to give some thought to the approaching duo-centenary celebrations. Many suggestions were forthcoming and in 1968 a committee was appointed to consider all the proposals and to make recommendations. The members of the committee were the President ex-officio, the Hon. Treasurer, the Assistant Hon. Treasurer, and three members, John Palmer, George Wilson, and Rear Admiral Garth Watson. The sum available in the Duo-Centenary Fund had reached £1,595 by December 1970, and for 1971 a special levy of £7 10s was added to the annual subscription in place of the 10s which each member had paid into the fund every year since 1960. A sum in excess of £2,000 was the target.

Among the matters considered by the committee was the provision of a history of the Society. One suggestion was to reprint Sydney Donkin's 1937 paper, but this idea was dismissed as it was felt more appropriate for the history to be brought up-to-date. There were fears however that to commission a new comprehensive history might prove too costly, and as an alternative a new biography of Smeaton was suggested, as it would have a wider appeal outside the limited membership of the Society. The Hon. Treasurer had been approached by Michael Lee who had just completed a new biography of Smeaton, which was already with a publisher for consideration. The Assistant Hon. Treasurer read the proof but did not consider it suitable for adoption by the Society.

The best solution, the committee concluded, would be to wait for Professor Skempton's projected history of the Society which was expected to be published in about two years' time. The committee recommended that copies of the book, specially bound, be purchased and presented to each member of the Society and a commemorative bookmark enclosed with each copy. Part of the Duo-Centenary Fund was earmarked for this purpose. Meanwhile a pamphlet, "The Smeatonians, Duo-Centenary Notes of the Society of Civil Engineers", was written by Professor Skempton and produced for the

OMNIA · IN · NUMERO · PONDERE · ET · MENSURA

SMEATONIAN SOCIETY
of
CIVIL ENGINEERS

Founded 1771

DUO-CENTENARY YEAR 1971

PRESIDENT:
H.R.H. PRINCE PHILIP, THE DUKE OF EDINBURGH, K.G., P.C., K.T., F.R.S.

FIRST CLASS MEMBERS   "ENGINEERS"

1937	M. T. TUDSBERY, C.B.E., F.C.G.I.	49, Hallam Street, London, W.1.
1941	THOMAS EDWIN HAWKSLEY, B.A.	1, Great Scotland Yard, Westminster, S.W.1.
1942	SIR ALLAN S. QUARTERMAINE, C.B.E., M.C., B.Sc.	53, Westminster Gardens, Marsham Street, S.W.1.
„	SIR BRUCE G. WHITE, K.B.E., F.C.G.I.	1, Lygon Place, Grosvenor Gardens, S.W.1.
1947	SIR JOHN G. WRIGHTSON, Bt., T.D., D.L.	Teesdale House, 16/26, Baltic Street, E.C.1.
1952	SIR WILLIAM H. GLANVILLE, C.B., C.B.E., D.Sc., F.R.S.	Langthwaite, Kewferry Drive, Northwood, Middx.
1953	GEOFFREY M. BINNIE, M.A.	Artillery House, Artillery Row, Westminster, S.W.1.
1954	R. W. MOUNTAIN, B.Sc.	Alliance House, 12, Caxton Street, S.W.1.
1956	SIR HAROLD HARDING, B.Sc., F.C.G.I., D.I.C.	79, Mount Ephraim, Tunbridge Wells, Kent.
1957	J. E. G. PALMER, M.A.	125, Victoria Street, Westminster, S.W.1.
„	H. D. MORGAN, M.Sc.	Newcombe House, 45, Notting Hill Gate, London, W.11.
„	R. W. HAWKEY, M.A.	9, Albany Court, Oatlands Drive, Weybridge, Surrey.
„	SIR VICTOR SHEPHEARD, K.C.B.	Manor Place, Manor Park, Chislehurst, Kent.
„	VICE-ADMIRAL SIR FRANK MASON, K.C.B.	Townfield House, 114, High Street, Hurstpierpoint, Sussex.
„	SIR ROBERT WYNNE-EDWARDS, C.B.E., D.S.O., M.C.	The Old House, The Close, Blandford, Dorset.
1958	G. A. WILSON, M.Eng.	Brandon House, North End Avenue, London, N.W.3.
„	SIR HAROLD BISHOP, C.B.E., B.Sc., F.C.G.I.	Carbis, Harborough Hill, Pulborough, Sussex.
1959	J. DUVIVIER, B.Sc., F.C.G.I.	4, Dean's Yard, Westminster, London, S.W.1.
1960	R. A. RIDDLES, C.B.E.	Grants House, Castlefield, Calne, Wilts.
„	M. G. R. SMITH, M.B.E.	4, Bendrick Drive, Southgate, Gower, South Wales.
„	SIR HENRY JONES, K.B.E.	Pathacres, Weston Turville, Aylesbury, Bucks.
„	SIR RALPH FREEMAN, C.V.O., C.B.E., M.A.	c/o Freeman, Fox & Partners, 25, Victoria Street, S.W.1.
1961	R. le G. HETHERINGTON, O.B.E., M.A.	28, Denewood Road, Highgate, London, N.6.
1962	T. A. L. PATON, C.M.G., B.Sc., F.R.S.	Telford House, 14, Tothill Street, S.W.1.
„	GODFREY T. VERRALL, M.A.	Furzeney, Fulmer, Bucks.
„	F. L. GORDON	22, Hanover House, St. John's Wood, London, N.W.8.
1963	PROFESSOR A. W. SKEMPTON, D.Sc., F.R.S.	16, The Boltons, Kensington, S.W.10.
„	D. C. COODE	2, Victoria Street, London, S.W.1.
1966	J. H. JELLETT, O.B.E., M.A.	30, Bassett Wood Drive, Southampton, Hants.
„	R. GLOSSOP	c/o John Mowlem & Co., Westgate House, Ealing Road, Brentford, Middx.
„	SIR ERIC YARROW, Bt., M.B.E.	Scotstoun, Glasgow, W.4.
„	SIR WILLIAM HARRIS, K.B.E., C.B.	5, Moor Park Road, Northwood, Middx.
„	SIR GILBERT ROBERTS, B.Sc., F.R.S., F.C.G.I.	Alliance House, Caxton Street, S.W.1.
„	A. H. CANTRELL, E.R.D., B.Sc.	12, Addington Road, South Croydon, Surrey, CR2 8RB.
1967	SIR ERIC MENSFORTH, C.B.E.	Speedicut Works, Carlisle Street East, Sheffield, 4.
„	P. W. E. HOLLOWAY, C.B.E., M.A., F.I.C.E.	Millbank House, 171/185, Ewell Road, Surbiton, Surrey.
„	J. W. BAXTER, B.Sc.	71, Barnfield Wood Road, Beckenham, Kent.
„	ROLAND C. BOND	Flint Cottage, Pinkneys Green, nr. Maidenhead, Berks.
„	O. A. KERENSKY, C.B.E.	Freeman Fox & Partners, Highways Engineering Dept., Abford House, 15, Wilton Road, S.W.1.
1968	Dr. K. C. DUNHAM, F.R.S.	29, Bolton Gardens, S.W.5.
„	SIR ALFRED SIMS, K.C.B., O.B.E.	Crosslands, Bannerdown Road, Batheaston, Bath.
„	REAR-ADMIRAL J. G. WATSON, C.B.	The Institution of Civil Engineers, Great George Street, S.W.1.
1969	SIR HUBERT SHIRLEY-SMITH, C.B.E., B.Sc.	70, Broxbourne Road, Orpington, Kent.
„	SIR KIRBY LAING, M.A., J.P.	John Laing and Son Limited, London, N.W.7.
1970	VICE-ADMIRAL R. G. RAPER, C.B.	Director General Ships, Ministry of Defence (Navy) Foxhill, Bath.
„	A. PATERSON, F.I.C.E.	240, Grove End Gardens, N.W.8.
1971	A. J. HARRIS, C.B.E.	127, Victoria Street, Westminster, London, S.W.1.
„	SIR EDWIN McALPINE	40, Bernard Street, London, W.C.1.

48

HONORARY MEMBERS   "GENTLEMEN"

1950	THE RT. HON. LORD HURCOMB OF CAMPDEN HILL, G.C.B., K.B.E.	47, Campden Hill Court, Kensington, W.8.
„	KENNETH S. CARPMAEL, Q.C.	Queen Elizabeth Building, Temple, E.C.4.
„	SIR EUSTACE GERVAIS TENNYSON D'EYNCOURT, Bt.	39, Upper Brook Street, W.1.
1953	H.R.H. PRINCE PHILIP THE DUKE OF EDINBURGH, K.G., P.C., K.T., F.R.S.	Buckingham Palace.
1954	SIR HUMPHREY BROWNE, C.B.E.	Beckbury Hall, Shifnal, Shropshire.
1960	CECIL R. C. TURNER	66, Queen Street, London, E.C.4.
1967	EDWARD I. HALLIDAY, R.P., R.B.A., A.R.C.A.(London)	62, Hamilton Terrace, St. John's Wood, N.W.8.
1969	JUDGE MERVYN GRIFFITH-JONES, Q.C.	Central Criminal Court, City of London, E.C.4.
1970	MAJOR J. RENNIE MAUDSLAY, C.V.O., M.B.E.	Privy Purse Office, Buckingham Palace.
„	THE RT. HON. VISCOUNT SIMON, C.M.G.	Port of London Authority, Trinity Square, London, E.C.3
„	THE RT. HON. MR. JUSTICE GRAHAM	The Royal Courts of Justice, Strand, W.C.2.
1971	MAJOR GENERAL R. L. CLUTTERBUCK, O.B.E., M.A., F.I.C.E.	Imperial Defence College, 37, Belgrave Square, London, S.W.1.

List of members, 1971

Society by the Institution of Civil Engineers, to be used during the Duo-Centenary year.

Dinner at the Junior Carlton Club was popular, and there was strong support for a return there as soon as accommodation could be made available. The food and wine were good, and the Disraeli "banjo" table was an added attraction: the only drawback was the lack of adequate assembly space for pre-dinner drinks. The United Service Club had its supporters too, and so for 1971 it was proposed to hold the January, February and March dinners at the "Senior" and the April, May and June dinners at the Junior Carlton. The special duo-centenary functions were to be additional to the regular programme. HRH Prince Philip, honorary member, became President of the Society for the duo-centenary year, and members were hopeful that he would preside at the main event, a banquet to be held in June.

The first event was a reception and buffet supper to which ladies were invited, and which was held at the house of the Royal Society, Carlton House Terrace, on Wednesday, 19 May. The main event was the banquet on 3 June, at the Fishmongers' Hall, which Sir Gervais Tennyson D'Eyncourt, a senior member of the Court of the Worshipful Company, had helped to arrange. In addition to 30 official guests, the fund provided for each member to bring a personal guest, and as far as the capacity of the hall allowed a second guest could be invited if paid for; altogether 180 attended.

Prince Philip who had been elected President for the year, presided and the official guests included the Lord Mayor of London, Sir Peter Studd; the Archbishop of York, Dr Donald Coggan; the Bishop of London, Dr R. W. Stopford; Viscount Radcliffe, a Lord of Appeal; and Lord Justice Salmon. Sir William Armstrong, Head of the Civil Service, Vice Admiral Anthony Griffin, Controller of the Navy, and Professor Alan Hodgkin, President of the Royal Society, attended. The Prime Warden of the Fishmongers Company and the Presidents of the Institutions of Civil, Mechanical and Electrical Engineers were all invited.

The 200 year life of the Society was also celebrated in more tangible ways. The longest serving member and senior Past President, Marmaduke Tudsbery, commissioned a most generous gift, a silver representation of the Eddystone Lighthouse, executed by Leslie Durbin, MVO, LLD, which was gratefully accepted to occupy an honoured place on the top table at dinner. Geoffrey Binnie, the President in 1970, gave the Society a silver water jug inscribed with the toast that members drink "To Waterworks". The vote of thanks for this gift, proposed by the Hon. Treasurer, was seconded by Robin

Riddles: he suggested that filling it with wine might prove too expensive so it might be wise to fill it with water as intended. Geoffrey Binnie's reply included the verse:

"Water is the best of things that man to man can bring.
But who am I that I should have the best of everything?
Let Princes revel at the Pump and Kings with springs make free.
But whisky, wine and even beer is good enough for me".

Apart from the two special events, the dinners in January, February, April and May during 1971 were all held at the Junior Carlton Club; those in 1972 all took place at the United Service Club.

Lord Mais, honorary member, took office as the Lord Mayor of London in November 1972 and invited the Society to dine at the Mansion House during his year of office. Arrangements were made for the dinner to be held on 14 June 1973. It was another memorable occasion in the long history of the Society.

The Duo-Centenary Fund had met all its commitments. Some £700 remained invested in 7% British Savings Bonds, against the time when the history of the Society would be published, and there was a cash balance of £36 which was transferred to the general funds. For several years the annual subscription had been £3 to include a contribution of 10s to the Fund. From 1972 the subscription was again reduced to £2 10s (or £2.50 following decimalisation).

At the meeting in December 1973 the President, Sir Harold Harding, let it be known that he and the Past Presidents had gone to some trouble to think of a way of celebrating Sir John Wrightson's 25 years as Hon. Treasurer, only to find that Sir John's service to the Society greatly exceeded that period: in fact he was first appointed in December 1936. Sir John was taken by surprise and at his suggestion the matter was deferred for the time being.

The 250th anniversary of John Smeaton's birth was celebrated at a service of commemoration in the parish church of St Mary, Whitkirk, in the summer of 1974. At the same time an exhibition was staged to mark the event in the museum at Leeds, his native city. Both events were attended by the President of the Society, John Palmer, and the Hon. Treasurer. Renewed interest in Smeaton and the origins of the engineering profession brought to attention the fact that, whereas the lives of the early 19th century engineers such as Telford, Watt, the Stephensons and others had been commemorated by the award of medals sponsored by the Engineering Institutions, the 18th century engineers had received no similar recognition.

It was suggested to the Council of Engineering Institutions, which, like the Society, embraced all disciplines of engineering, that a John

Smeaton Medal be introduced in this his anniversary year, to be awarded for outstanding engineering achievement. The first meeting of the Smeaton Awards Committee, under the auspices of the CEI, was held in November 1974. The chairman of this joint Committee was Sir Angus Paton and the Society was represented by the President, Professor Skempton and the Hon. Treasurer, for whom Cecil Turner acted. Early meetings were concerned with drafting terms of reference, judgement procedure and administrative arrangements. An artist was commissioned for the design, and the medal was struck.

The first award of the Smeaton Gold Medal was made in 1974 to Geoffrey Morse Binnie, a Past President of the Society, the senior

Water jug and Eddystone Lighthouse

Smeaton Medal and silver salver

partner in the consulting engineers Binnie and Partners, "for his outstanding contribution to Civil Engineering". The presentation was made by the Chairman of the CEI, Professor John Coales, at a ceremony in the Brunel Room of the Institution of Civil Engineers, preceding the AGM of the Society in November 1975. The 1975 medal was awarded to Sir Stanley Hooker, Technical Director of Rolls Royce Ltd, for the development of advanced aero-engine design; and the 1977 award was given to Sir Leonard Renshaw, Managing Director of Vickers Shipbuilding and Engineering Co. Ltd, Barrow-in-Furness, who had designed and built the first British nuclear powered submarine, *HMS Dreadnought*.

In November 1975 when he handed over as President of the Society, Reginald Hawkey said that he wished to give the Society some token in recognition of all the friendship and pleasure he had enjoyed throughout his years of membership: he also felt that there should be in the Society some permanent record of the winners of the Smeaton Medal. Putting these ideas together he presented a silver salver which incorporated a copy of the medal at its centre to be inscribed with the names of the winners; Geoffrey Binnie's name had already been engraved upon it.

Grave concern for the future of the Society was expressed at the AGM in November 1974. Attendance at meetings in the 1974 session had dropped by an average of ten compared with 1973. A reduction in the number of meetings was suggested; two in the spring and two in the autumn might be better attended than six in six months. One factor was thought to be that the cost of an overnight stay in London had risen markedly, making it more difficult for out-of-town members to attend. It was also thought that the older members, through declining health or retirement from active professional engagement, were finding regular attendance increasingly difficult.

Sir Harold Harding suggested that younger rather than older new members should be elected to the Society, and added that if any member felt he could hardly ever come to dinner it would be graceful for him to resign and make way for a younger person. His view was supported by the Hon. Treasurer, who said he felt this had not been borne in mind by the proposers of the candidates they were about to consider.

Inflation was taking its toll: the Society's costs were rising, but the basic subscription had remained the same for 30 years. The books had only been balanced by the generosity of two anonymous donors, and there was a strong feeling that the Society should not have to depend on such gifts; a substantial increase in subscriptions was necessary. This brought under discussion once again the subscription paid by honorary members. Two rates were suggested, one for first class members and a reduced one for honorary members but this was rejected; the honorary members were an integral part of the Society and should be treated as such, said the Hon. Treasurer.

An entrance fee was proposed, but it was decided instead to make it a condition of entry that a copy of the facsimile Minute Book be purchased at a price of £10. As a result of the discussion the number of dinners was reduced to four, two in the spring and two in the autumn, and two luncheons were added; those arranged by John Rennie during the war had been well attended and for some would avoid an overnight stay in London. The annual subscription was increased to £7.50 for both classes of members.

Despite the drop in attendance, the popularity of membership of the Society was not in doubt. From 1958 to 1968 the average number of vacancies for first class membership at each ballot was three and the number of candidates ranged from six to eight, but 1970 was exceptional; there were 14 candidates for two vacancies. In these circumstances the maintenance of a broad range of disciplines, a tradition of the Society, was difficult to achieve.

During 1975, the four dinners were held at the Institution of Civil Engineers and the two luncheons took place at the Carlton Club, St James Street, but the total number of attendances continued its downward trend; from 260 in 1974 to 163 in 1975. The luncheons were poorly attended, although those who were at them said they much appreciated them. However, it was felt it was too soon to draw conclusions, and it was agreed to repeat the same pattern of meetings in 1976.

Sir John Wrightson informed the President that he would be retiring from his company in June 1976, and that Head, Wrightson & Co Ltd. would no longer be able to support the secretarial work of the Society which they had been undertaking so generously for the past 38 years. The Secretary of the Institution of Civil Engineers agreed to the Institution undertaking some of the secretarial work, and Miss Hilda Hooker took over from Miss Margaret Folliard. Before the AGM began in December, the President, Sir Victor Shepheard, made a presentation to Miss Folliard on behalf of the members. For more than 23 years she had carried out the secretarial work of the Society and this was the opportunity for the members to express their gratitude.

Sir John Wrightson agreed to continue in office as Hon. Treasurer for another year or so, but as he would be spending less time in London, a small committee was formed, at his suggestion, to oversee the running of the Society's affairs. It comprised the President for the year and the two members next in line for the Presidency, the Hon. Treasurer and the Assistant Hon. Treasurer.

There were two vacancies for honorary members in December 1976, but it was not intended that they should be filled immediately. Members were asked to give careful consideration to whom they might propose. Candidates should be members of other professions, the law, the church, the arts, medicine, the armed forces, for example, but with an interest in science and engineering, as required by the Rules; above all they must be good company and have an interest in the Society. The hope was expressed that nominations would be from a wider circle than had been forthcoming in recent years. An election took place in February, but there was only one candidate and he was duly elected.

In the following November there were still no vacancies for first class members but there were three for honorary members and this time there were six nominations. However, three of the six were chartered engineers, and a discussion ensued about their eligibility.

Sir Harold Harding   *Professor A. W. Skempton*

The Assistant Hon. Treasurer, speaking, he said, not as an honorary member but as the Assistant Hon. Treasurer for over 20 years and as a lawyer, thought members would agree that if the Society selected "Gentlemen" rather than "Engineers" for first class membership, the Society would be in breach of its Rules and traditions. If this was accepted, then it would be very difficult not to accept the corollary, i.e. that it was in breach of the Rules and traditions of the Society to elect as an honorary member a candidate who was an engineer. The nominations of the three engineers were then withdrawn by their sponsors and the three "Gentlemen" were elected.

Messages of loyalty and good wishes to the Queen and Prince Philip were sent to His Royal Highness on behalf of the Society on the occasion of Her Majesty's Silver Jubilee. In his reply, Prince Philip expressed his concern for the general welfare of engineers and engineering, particularly during these difficult times, and hoped that a close relationship would develop between the Society and the Fellowship of Engineering. The Society celebrated the Queen's Jubilee by holding a ladies' night at the Institution of Civil Engineers on 25 May 1977. The members and their ladies were received by the President, Vice Admiral Sir Frank Mason, and Lady Mason.

When the programme of meetings for 1978 was discussed there was strong support for a return to the traditional arrangement of six dinners between January and June, the old Parliamentary session.

Luncheons had not been well attended, although they undoubtedly suited some people. As a compromise it was decided to hold five dinners between January and May and a luncheon in November/ December preceding the AGM; all would be held at the Institution of Civil Engineers. Sir John Wrightson's resignation as Hon. Treasurer was announced at the AGM in December 1978. During the 42 years he had served the Society, first as Secretary and then as Hon. Treasurer, he had found the work stimulating, he said, and had made many friends; he was sad to be giving up office, but he had retired, had no permanent office in London and his visits to London were infrequent. The time had come to hand-over.

His successor was Cecil Turner, who agreed to accept the post of Hon. Treasurer for a limited period and took over on 14 January 1979. James Wiltshire, a first class member and a partner in the firm founded by Sir Alexander Kennedy, was invited to become Assistant Hon. Treasurer.

Now was the time to celebrate Sir John Wrightson's long service to the Society. A dinner was held at the Army and Navy Club, Pall Mall, on 6 December 1978, to which Sir John and Lady Wrightson were invited and members were accompanied by their ladies. HRH Prince Philip attended, and the President Sir Ralph Freeman and Lady Freeman received the members and their guests. A commemorative scroll, addressed to Sir John and signed by all the members of the Society, was presented to him in the course of the evening.

The future of the secretarial work of the Society came under discussion again in January 1979. The Institution wished to be relieved of the work, in view of the increasing calls upon its secretarial services and the impending retirement of its Secretary. James Wiltshire, the Assistant Hon. Treasurer, agreed that there would be advantages in transferring the work to his office, and with the agreement of the President and the committee, Mrs Margaret Beaney took over the secretarial work from Miss Hooker in April.

It was the custom for the President to propose his successor for election at the AGM and it had become the practice for him to nominate the member next in seniority by year of election to membership. Roger Hetherington was approached with a view to being the President in 1979 but he declined on grounds of ill health. Cecil Turner, who had become an honorary member in the same year, was nominated and elected, once again combining the offices of President and Hon. Treasurer.

In 1979 the annual subscription was still £7.50, but the effect of inflation had made it necessary to increase the members' contributions to the cost of dinner to maintain a satisfactory standard. The

OMNIA · IN · NUMERO · PONDERE · ET · MENSURA

SMEATONIAN SOCIETY
OF
CIVIL ENGINEERS

Founded 1771

Know ye all men that by these presents

Whereas Sir John Garmondsway Wrightson Baronet was appointed Honorary Secretary to the Society on and from the first day of December 1936, was elected a First Class Member of the Society in 1947 and was promoted Honorary Treasurer in 1949, which post he has held ever since and continues to hold, and has thus served the Society in an honorary executive capacity for a continuous period in excess of forty years

And Whereas it is the unanimous opinion of the other members that during the said period the said John Wrightson has at all times afforded to the Society and to the successive Presidents thereof the benefit of loyal and wise guidance and service and thereby earned the lasting respect and admiration of the Society

Now Therefore we the other members of the Society, present and absent, have hereunto subscribed our names as a mark of our respect and admiration as aforesaid this sixth day of December one thousand nine hundred and seventy eight.

Honorary Members

First Class Members

Scroll presented to Sir John Wrightson

in the activities of the Society. These proposals were approved in principle and referred to the Presidents' Committee to which Sir William was co-opted. A postal ballot of all first class members was overwhelmingly in favour. The resolutions and motion were passed and the new class came into being in November 1980.

The Presidents' Committee, which from its formation in 1976 had played an important but informal part in the affairs of the Society, was given a specific task under the rules regulating transfers to Membership Emeritus, and its constitution was confirmed in the motion passed by the members. The inclusion of a President designate was questioned for uncertainty, but as it had become the custom to choose the President from the list of first class members in order of their election to membership, no difficulty was expected to arise in identifying the President designate. From November 1980 all doubt was removed when it became the practice to nominate the President designate at the same time as electing the President.

Cecil Turner, who had served the Society with devotion for 25 years and given practical assistance in the offices of Assistant Hon. Treasurer and Hon. Treasurer, tendered his resignation from office in November 1980. He proposed as his successor James Wiltshire, the Assistant Hon. Treasurer, who was elected unanimously. Sir John Wrightson, with whom Cecil Turner had worked closely for many years, proposed a heartfelt vote of thanks to him, which the members supported with acclamation.

Four Members Emeritus were appointed in January 1981: they were Marmaduke Tudsbery, by far the longest serving member, having been elected in 1937; Sir Harold Harding, elected in 1956; John Palmer and Sir Henry Jones, both of whom had resigned prior to 1980. The elevation of two serving members to Members Emeritus and the deaths of two others created four vacancies for first class members in January. The President again stressed the desirability of nominating some younger men and engineers from as wide a range of disciplines as possible. To this end a list showing the disciplines of existing members was issued.

Two more deaths and two resignations produced four more vacancies for first class membership to be filled at the AGM in November 1981 for which there were 15 candidates. According to the Rules, when there are several candidates for each vacancy the first ballot would reduce the number to two for each vacancy by discarding those with the least votes. It left open the question of whether at the first ballot, members should vote for the same number of candidates as vacancies or twice the number. At the meeting it was decided to vote for the actual number of vacancies in both ballots.

PROFESSIONAL PRACTICE

Industry General	3
Construction Industry	6
Consulting	18
Defence	3
Govt. and Nationalised Industries	10
Academic	7

DISCIPLINE IN ENGINEERING

Civil Engineering – general	9
Structural	5
Highways and Bridges	5
Water	3
Dams	3
Marine Structures	7
Railways	4
Geological & Soil Mechanics	2
Mechanical	3
Electrical	4
Naval Architecture and Marine Engineering	4
Aeronautical	NIL

Fellows of Royal Society	6
Fellows of Fellowship of Engineering	27

Note: Inevitably some members are in more than one category.

Analysis of first class membership, December 1980

R U L E S

OF THE

SMEATONIAN SOCIETY OF CIVIL ENGINEERS

FOUNDED 1771

I. That (subject to the provisions of Rule XVII below) the Society shall consist of Two Classes of Members.

II. That the First Class shall consist of Engineers only, and that no person shall become a Member thereof except those who are actually employed in Surveying, Designing, and forming Works of different kinds in various departments of Civil Engineering. The number in this class to be limited to forty-eight.

III. That the Second Class shall consist of Gentlemen under the denomination of Honorary Members, and that any person shall be eligible for election as an Honorary Member who is conversant with the theory or practice of the several branches of science necessary to the profession of a Civil Engineer; the number in this Class to be limited to twelve.

IV. That five Members of the First Class shall form a quorum for business.

V. That there shall be an Annual General Meeting of Members and Hon. Members for the purpose of electing new Members and transacting other business. This meeting shall take place on the last Wednesday in June or at any other date convenient to the Members. A Special General Meeting shall be called at any time on the written request of any five Members, stating the purpose for which the meeting is required.

VI. That at the Annual General Meeting or at any Special General Meeting, the Society may proceed to elect a president for the following Season, who, having served that office during the Session, shall not be eligible for re-election again for two years.

VII. That all Members shall be elected by ballot either at the Annual General Meeting or at any Special General Meeting. When there are several candidates for each vacancy, those candidates receiving the lowest number of votes at the first ballot shall be eliminated, so as to reduce the number to Two candidates for each vacancy. At the second ballot, the candidate or candidates receiving the greatest number of votes shall be elected. Further ballots to take place in the event of an equal number of votes being received by any two or more candidates. The vacancies to which new members may be elected shall be the number that obtained twenty-one days before the Meeting. Not more than six members of the First Class of Membership shall be elected at any meeting.

VIII. Every Member who wishes to propose a candidate for the election shall do so in writing. The proposal, seconded in writing, must be sent to the Hon. Treasurer not less than twenty-one days before the Annual General Meeting or any Special General Meeting convened for the purpose of electing Members. A list of the candidates proposed and the names of their proposers and seconders, shall be sent by the Hon. Treasurer to all Members not later than fourteen days before the Meeting at which the election is to take place. No ballot papers shall be given to any Members not present at this Meeting. In the event of a vacancy either in the number of Members or Honorary Members remaining after the ballot, further ballots may be taken to fill the vacancy.

IX. That each newly elected Member shall pay his subscription, and attend within one twelve months from the day of his election, and if he fails to do so he shall cease to be a member of the Society.

X. That candidates proposed and not elected, may, on a subsequent occasion, be proposed and seconded again as provided in Rule VII.

XI. That an annual contribution, payable in January, the amount of which shall be determined in each year by the Hon. Treasurer, be collected from all the Members of the Society to defray the fixed and general expenses. That the name of any Member, whose contribution is in arrear for the current and preceding year, shall, with the consent of the Annual General Meeting, be removed from the List of Members.

XII. That the President do take the chair at all meetings of the Society, and that in case of his absence, the chair to be taken by such member as may be selected at the time.

XIII. That in case any Member be desirous of introducing a friend, he be at liberty to invite him, upon his paying such subscription as may be agreed upon for the dinner.

XIV. That a Member of the First Class of this Society shall, on proper occasions, assume the style and title of "Member of the Smeatonian Society of Civil Engineers".

XV. That the meetings of this Society be held on a Wednesday, at the latter end of the months of January, February, March, April, May and June or at any other date convenient to the Members.

XVI. That no regulation or alterations of the existing Rules shall be valid unless decided upon at the Annual General Meeting or at a Special General Meeting, and no such regulation or alteration shall be considered unless it has been sent in writing by the Proposer to the Hon. Treasurer not less than fourteen days and by him to all members not less than seven days before the Annual General Meeting or the Special General Meeting.

XVII. That in addition to the Two Classes of Members referred to in Rule 1 above a new Class of Membership under the title of Membership Emeritus was formed under certain Special Resolutions of the Society passed on the 24th day of October 1980 with admission thereto open to Members of the First Class of this Society upon and always subject to such terms, conditions and requirements as are in the Special Resolutions contained. The number in this Class (in addition to the forty-eight in the First Class) to be limited to **twelve**.

XVIII. That by a Motion of the Society adopted and confirmed at the Annual General Meeting held on the 26th day of November, 1980 executive powers necessary for the purpose of operating the admission to the Membership Emeritus but for no other purpose were vested in a Committee meeting under the title of "The President's Committee" and founded upon such composition, terms and conditions as are in the Motion contained.

Rules of the Society, 1988

members to miss the opportunity of discussing with the sponsors of candidates the eligibility of those with whom they were not personally acquainted. The resolution was negatived.

Although membership was much sought after, once elected the attendance of some members was not all it might be. The Presidents' Committee considered what might be done. Some of those who had allowed their attendance to lapse were approached on behalf of the committee, not with the aim of seeking resignations (although one or two followed) but with a view to a renewal of participation in the activities of the Society.

There are no rules requiring regular attendance or enabling the Society to take action in respect of absentees, and although the committee thought this unfortunate when the membership of each class was so restricted, the policy of not inviting resignations was endorsed. The introduction of Members Emeritus had created more opportunities for the election of first class members than would have existed otherwise. Nevertheless the future of the Society depended primarily on the regular attendance of members in all classes, and when, for good reason, members are unable to attend, the committee felt that the way should be opened for the admission of other, especially younger, members, if the traditions of the Society were to be maintained.

The admission of new younger members of all engineering disciplines is a perennial problem, but all agreed that it is not a matter for any changes in the Rules but for action by the members themselves, whenever the occasion arises.

Famous Families

Several families of famous engineers have links with the Smeatonians which go back through many generations. The Rennies, Mylnes, Donkins and Hawksleys are among them.

Member	Treas.	Pres.		Born	Died
1785	1812	–	John Rennie	1761	1821
1822	–	1844	George Rennie, eldest son of John	1791	1866
1822	–	1841, 1855	Sir John Rennie, second son of John	1794	1874
1860	1883	1873	George Banks Rennie, son of George	1832	1908
1901	1903	1927	John Assheton Rennie, son of George Banks	1876	1949
1771	1793	–	Robert Mylne	1734	1811
1811	1822	1842, 1859	William Chadwell Mylne, second son of Robert	1781	1863
1845	1864	–	Robert William Mylne, son of William Chadwell	1817	1890
1835	–	1843	Bryan Donkin	1768	1855
–	–	–	John Donkin, eldest son of Bryan	1802	1854
1859	–	1872	Bryan Donkin, fifth son of Bryan	1809	1893
–	–	–	Bryan Donkin, eldest son of John	1835	1902
1931	–	1949	Sydney Bryan Donkin, son of Bryan	1871	1952
1872	–	1885	Thomas Hawksley	1807	1893
1897	–	1911	Charles Hawksley, son of Thomas	1839	1917
1920	–	–	Kenneth Phipson Hawksley, son of Charles	1869	1924
1941	–	1958	Thomas Edwin Hawksley, son of Kenneth	1897	1972

The Members

Honorary Members' names are shown in italics; an asterisk indicates a Member Emeritus.

The names listed are those of members at the time of their election to membership; the titles and designations of many changed later when they acquired further honours and awards. Dates of resignation, where applicable, are not shown.

In 1793 the Society was reconstructed without a President. However, in 1841 it was resolved "That it is expedient that the Society do annually elect a President". There were no Presidents in 1880, 1915–18 or in 1940.

Dates before September 1752 are "new style".

Member	President		Born	Died
1771	1771	Thomas Yeoman	1708	1781
		John Smeaton	1724	1792
		Robert Mylne	1733	1811
	1783	Joseph Nickalls	1725	1793
		John Grundy	1719	1783
		John Thompson	–	–
		J. King	–	–
		John Golborne	1724	1783
		Robert Whitworth	1734	1799
		William Black	–	–
		Hugh Henshall	1734	1816
1772		John Smith	–	–
		William Iveson	1728	1786
		John Holmes	1727	1797
		William Mathews	–	–
		Thomas Hogarth	–	1783
1773		William Jessop	1745	1814
		Langley Edwards	–	1774
		Joseph Priestly	1741	1817
		John Longbottom	–	1801
		John Gott	1720	1793
1774		Joseph Page	–	–

Member	President		Born	Died
1774		Robert McHale	–	–
		Major Henry Watson	1737	1786
	1781	Christopher Pinchbeck	1710	1783
		William De Brahm	1717	1799
		William Thompson	–	–
		John Monk	–	1775
1776		Murdoch McKenzie	1712	1797
		Robert Hanum	–	–
		Thomas Fruin	–	–
		Edward Gascoigne	–	1785
		John Cowper	1742	1792
		William Faden	1749	1836
		Samuel Phillips	–	1811
1777		John Jardin	–	1801
		Thomas Morris	–	–
		Reuben Hodgkinson	–	–
		John Pinkerton	–	1813
		John Pierce	1724	1792
1778		Edward Nairne	1726	1806
		Thomas Walford	–	1790
1780		James Cowper	–	1801
		Matthew Boulton	1728	1809
		John Whitehurst	1713	1788
		Graham Wilkinson	–	–
		Luke Hogard	–	–
1781		Reuben Burrow	1747	1792
		Thomas Martin	–	–
		James Arrow	–	1791
		William Thomas	–	1800
		Samuel Wyatt	1737	1807
1782		Stephen Nickson	–	–
		James Northcoate, RA	1746	1831
1783		John Snape	1738	1816
		Dr Butler, DD	–	–
		Thomas Dadford	–	1809
1785		John Rennie	1761	1821
1786		George Young	1750	1820
1789		Henry Eastburn	1753	1821
		James Watt	1736	1819
		John Marquand	1723	1810
		Joseph Jacob	–	–
1791		James Playfair	1755	1794
		Rev. Henry Green	1728	1797
1792		*Charles Alexander Craig*	–	–
		Joseph Hodskinson	1735	1801

Member	President		Born	Died
1793		James Golborne	1746	1819
		Sir Thomas Hyde Page	1746	1821
		John Duncombe	–	1810
		Thomas Milne	–	–
		Jesse Ramsden	1735	1800
		John Troughton	1739	1807
		John Foulds	1742	1815
		Samuel Brook	1746	1798
		Sir Joseph Banks, Bart	1744	1820
		Colonel Samuel Bentham	1757	1831
		Major Rennell	–	–
		George Maxwell	1744	1816
		Sir George Shuckburgh, Bart	1751	1804
1794		Joseph Huddart	1741	1816
		Dr Charles Hutton	1737	1823
1795		William Chapman	1749	1832
		John Watté	–	–
		James Cockshutt	1742	1819
		Henry Oxenden	1756	1838
1796		*The Earl of Morton*	1761	1827
		John Lloyd	1749	1815
1797		*Hon. Charles Greville*	1749	1809
1798		*Jean Louis Barallier*	1751	–
		Charles Hatchett	1765	1847
		George Dance, RA	1741	1825
1799		*William Mudge*	1762	1820
		Richard Ellison, MP	1754	1827
		Benjamin Count Rumford	1753	1814
1800		*Peter Dolland*	1730	1820
		Alexander Aubert	1730	1805
		William Vaughan	1752	1850
1804		*Rev. Dr Nevil Maskelyne*	1732	1811
		Sir John Morris, Bart	1745	1819
		The Viscount Kirkwall	1778	1820
		Thomas Richard Beaumont, MP	1758	1829
1805		*William Parsons*	–	1828
		The Lord Dundas	1741	1820
1806		*Richard Lovell Edgeworth*	1744	1817
		Mark Beaufoy	1764	1827
		Hon. George Knox	1765	1827
		William Smith, MP	1756	1835
1808		*Sir William Herschel*	1738	1822
		Stephen Lee	–	–
		Humphry Davy	1778	1829
1809		Joseph Whidbey	1755	1833

Member	President		Born	Died
1810		*George Dollond*	1774	1852
		Edward Troughton	1753	1835
1811		*John George Children*	1777	1852
		Davies Giddy (Gilbert)	1767	1839
	1842, 1859	William Chadwell Mylne	1781	1863
1812		*Thomas Murdoch*	1757	1846
		Sir John Barrow, Bart	1764	1848
		Maj. Gen. John Garstin, RE	1756	1820
		John Pond	1767	1836
1813		Josias Jessop	1781	1826
1815		*Matthew Raper*	1741	1826
1822	1844	George Rennie	1791	1866
	1841, 1855	Sir John Rennie	1794	1874
		Daniel Moore	1759	1828
		Peter Ewart	1767	1842
		Sir Francis Chantrey	1781	1842
		Henry Browne	1753	1830
		Charles Babbage	1792	1871
		Maj. Gen. John Rowley, RE	1768	1824
		Col. Thomas Colby	1784	1852
		John Barton	1771	1834
		Sir Robert Seppings	1767	1840
		James Watt	1769	1848
1823		*Francis Baily*	1774	1844
	1849	*John Taylor*	1779	1863
		Captain Francis Beaufort, RN	1774	1857
1824	1852	James Walker	1781	1862
		Philip Taylor	1786	1870
		John Millington	1779	1868
		Captain Edward Sabine, RA	1788	1883
		Charles Stokes	1784	1853
1825		William Jessop	1783	1852
		William Woolrych Whitmore, MP	1787	1858
1827		James Jardine	1776	1858
		Robert Stevenson	1772	1850
		Captain Basil Hall, RN	1788	1844
		Captain John James Chapman, RA	1789	1867
		Lieut. Col. Charles William Pasley, RE	1780	1861
1828		Francis Giles	1787	1847
		Captain John Watson Pringle, RE	–	–
		Captain Joseph Portlock, RE	1794	1864
		Frederick Page	1769	1834

Member	President		Born	Died
1831	1845	William Cubitt	1785	1861
1832		William Tierney Clark	1783	1852
1835	1843	Bryan Donkin	1768	1855
	1848	Joshua Field	1787	1863
	1850	James Simpson	1799	1869
1836		Col. George Landmann, RE	1779	1854
		Joseph Miller	1797	1860
	1846	*Dr Peter Mark Roget, MD*	1779	1869
		Rev. William Whewell	1794	1866
1837		Marc Isambart Brunel	1769	1849
1838		John Macneill	1793	1880
		Captain Henry Brandreth, RE	–	–
1839		*Francis Bramah*	1785	1840
1841		Isambard Kingdom Brunel	1806	1859
		James Meadows Rendel	1799	1856
1842	1860	John Murray	1804	1882
		Jesse Hartley	1780	1860
		Joseph Glynn	1799	1863
		Edward Bury	1794	1858
1843	1858	Henry Wollaston Blake	1815	1899
1844		Joseph Cubitt	1811	1872
	1864	William Lindley	1808	1900
1845	1847, 1856	Robert Stephenson	1803	1859
		Joseph Locke	1805	1860
	1861	William Gravatt	1806	1866
		George Lowe	1788	1868
	1853, 1866	Charles Blacker Vignoles	1793	1875
		Charles Manby	1804	1884
		Robert William Mylne	1817	1890
1847		George Stephenson	1781	1848
1849		*Charles Hampden Turner*	1772	1856
	1851	Thomas Lloyd	1803	1875
		William Cotton	1786	1866
1851	1862	Charles Hutton Gregory	1817	1898
		Alfred Burges	1801	1886
	1865	Peter William Barlow	1809	1885
	1857	John Hawkshaw	1811	1891
		Alan Stevenson	1807	1865
	1854	*Joseph Baxendale*	1785	1872
	1863, 1891	*Captain John Linton Arabin Simmons, RE*	1821	1903
	1891			
		Professor George Biddell Airy	1801	1892
1853		David Stevenson	1815	1886

Member	President		Born	Died
	1868	John Fowler	1817	1898
		Michael Andrew Borthwick	1810	1856
1854	1869	John Penn	1805	1878
1856		William Simpson	1809	1864
		Robert Napier	1791	1876
1857		James Leslie	1801	1889
	1867	Alfred Giles	1816	1895
1858	1896	*Captain Douglas Galton, RE*	1823	1899
1859	1871	John Frederic La Trobe Bateman	1810	1889
	1872	Bryan Donkin	1809	1893
1860		Sir William Fairbairn, Bart	1789	1874
		Thomas Page	1803	1877
	1873	George Banks Rennie	1832	1908
1862		George Willoughby Hemans	1814	1885
		John Robinson McClean	1813	1873
1863	1870	*Col. William Francis Drummond Jervois, RE*	1821	1897
		Nathaniel Beardmore	1816	1872
		Maj. Gen. Francis Rawdon Chesney, RA	1789	1872
1864		Joseph Whitworth	1803	1887
		Sir William Armstrong	1810	1900
		Maj. Gen. Sir Andrew Scott Waugh, RE	1810	1878
1866	1875	William Henry Barlow	1812	1902
		John Coode	1816	1892
		Thomas Elliott Harrison	1808	1883
		George Fosbery Lyster	1821	1899
		The Earl of Caithness	1821	1881
	1874	*Dr John Percy, MD*	1817	1889
1867	1876	Joseph William Bazalgette	1819	1891
	1878	James Brunlees	1816	1892
		Captain Edward Bellfield, RE	1827	1921
	1877	James Abernethy	1814	1896
		Sir Daniel Gooch, Bart, MP	1816	1889
1868		*The Duke of Sutherland*	1828	1892
1869		Stephen William Leach	1818	1881
		Joseph Quick	1809	1894
	1879	Charles William Siemens	1828	1883
	1883	Sir Frederick (Joseph) Bramwell	1818	1903
	1881	*Warington Wilkinson Smyth*	1817	1890
1870	1882	George Barclay Bruce	1821	1908
		Joseph Mitchell	1803	1883
		Alexander Meadows Rendel	1827	1918
		Maj. Gen. John Henry Lefroy, RA	1817	1890

Member	President		Born	Died
1872	1884	Edward Woods	1814	1903
		William Baker	1817	1878
	1885	Thomas Hawksley	1807	1898
		Sir Charles Wheatstone	1802	1875
1874		Henry Bessemer	1813	1898
		George Berkley	1821	1893
		Alexander Moncrieff	1829	1906
		Clifford Wigram	1827	1894
		Admiral Sir Alexander Milne, Bart	1806	1896
		Col. Charles Pasley, RE	1824	1890
1875	1887	Robert Joseph Rawlinson	1810	1898
		Professor Dr William Pole	1814	1900
1876		Charles Greaves	1816	1883
	1889	John Clarke Hawkshaw	1841	1921
1877	1886	*Frederick Augustus Abel*	1827	1902
	1890	Richard Boxall Grantham	1805	1891
1878		Hutton Vignoles	1824	1889
	1888	*Col. William Crossman, RE*	1830	1901
		Maj. Gen. Charles Younghusband, RA	1821	1899
1879	1892	John Wolfe Barry	1836	1918
1880		Francis Stevenson	1827	1902
1882		James Nicholas Douglass	1826	1898
1883	1894	Benjamin Baker	1840	1907
		Thomas Russell Crampton	1816	1883
	1893	*Samuel Pope, QC*	1826	1901
	1895	Henry Marc Brunel	1842	1903
		General Sir Charles Nugent, RE	1827	1899
1884	1897	Frank McClean	1837	1904
	1898	William Henry Preece	1834	1913
		Vice Admiral Richard Vesey Hamilton	1829	1912
	1899	Captain Andrew Noble, RA	1831	1915
		Sir James (Joseph) Allport	1811	1892
1888		Sir Bradford Leslie	1831	1926
		Richard Sennett	1847	1891
		William Anderson	1835	1898
		Col. Eardley Maitland, RA	1833	1911
		Maj. Gen. Alexander de Courcy Scott, RE	1834	1899
1890	1900	William Henry White	1845	1913
	1901	Francis William Webb	1836	1906
		George Miller Cunningham	1829	1897
1891		James Mansergh	1834	1905
1892	1903	Percy George Buchanan Westmacott	1830	1917

Member	President		Born	Died
1892	1904	Alexander Richardson Binnie	1839	1917
1894	1905	George Chatterton	1853	1910
	1906	Alexander Siemens	1847	1928
	1907	George Neill Abernethy	1854	1923
	1902	*James Dewar*	1842	1923
1896		James Henry Greathead	1844	1896
	1909	George Frederick Deacon	1843	1909
		William Robert Galbraith	1829	1914
		Thomas Forster Brown	1835	1907
	1908	Professor Alexander Blackie William Kennedy	1847	1928
		Sir Edward Carbutt, Bart	1838	1905
		George Mair Rumley	1843	1920
	1910	Cuthbert Andrew Brereton	1851	1910
		Maj. Gen. Sir Charles Wilson, RE	1836	1905
		Dr Andrew Ainslie Common	1841	1903
		James Thompson	1835	1906
1897		William Matthews	1844	1922
	1911	Charles Hawksley	1839	1917
1898		Horace Bell	1839	1903
	1912	George Robert Jebb	1838	1927
	1913	Professor William Cawthorne Unwin	1838	1933
1899		Engineer Vice Admiral Sir John Durston	1846	1917
	1914	Philip Watts	1846	1926
		Frank Ewart Robertson	1847	1912
		George James Symons	1838	1900
1900		John Isaac Thornycroft	1843	1928
		Francis Elgar	1845	1909
	1920	Saxton William Armstrong Noble	1863	1942
1901		Rt Hon. William James Pirrie	1847	1924
		James Charles Inglis	1851	1911
	1921	John Strain	1845	1931
		Dr Ludwig Mond	1839	1909
	1927	John Assheton Rennie	1876	1949
		Henry Graham Harris	1850	1910
1903		John Allen McDonald	1847	1904
		Sir John Aird, Bart	1833	1911
	1922	Professor John Harvard Biles	1854	1933
		Sir Ralph (Daniel) Littler, KC	1835	1908
		Berkeley Paget	1841	1910
1904		Samuel George Homfrey	1855	1908
	1923	Robert Elliott-Cooper	1845	1942
	1924	Maurice Fitzmaurice	1861	1924
		Robert Abbott Hadfield	1858	1940

Member	President		Born	Died
1905		Hon. Charles Algernon Parsons	1854	1931
	1925	Alan Archibald Campbell Swinton	1863	1930
1906		William Wilkinson Squire	1854	1915
		Benjamin Hall Blyth	1849	1917
1907	1926	Henry Reginald Arnulph Mallock	1851	1933
1908		Edward Pritchard Martin	1844	1910
		Thomas Matthews	1849	1930
	1928	William Barton Worthington	1854	1939
1909		Robert White	1842	1925
		Anthony George Lyster	1852	1920
		Walter Hunter	1840	1914
	1929	Engineer Vice Admiral Henry John Oram	1858	1939
	1919	*John Hutton Balfour Browne, KC*	1845	1921
1910		Sir Thomas Wrightson, Bart	1839	1921
		Sir David Gill	1843	1914
		Edward Honoratus Lloyd, KC	1860	1930
1911	1930	John Henry Tudsbery Tudsbery	1859	1939
		Hay Frederick Donaldson	1856	1916
		Sir Frederick (Robert) Upcott	1847	1918
	1931	John Audley Frederick Aspinall	1851	1937
		Dugald Clerk	1854	1932
		Dr James Alfred Ewing	1855	1935
1912		Godfred Midgley Taylor	1861	1927
		James Swinburne	1858	1958
		Sir Archibald Geikie	1835	1924
		Captain Herbert Acton Blake, RN	1857	1926
		Gilbert Henry Claughton	1856	1921
		Col. Sir Thomas (Hungerford) Holdich, RE	1843	1929
		Sir Ernest (Henry) Shackleton	1874	1922
		Maj. Gen. Sir Desmond O'Callaghan, RA	1843	1931
1913		Col. Sir Edouard (Percy) Girouard, RE	1867	1932
	1932	Sir Archibald Denny, Bart	1860	1936
1913		Edward Bazzand Ellington	1845	1914
		Basil Mott	1859	1938
		Maj. Gen. Sir Charles (Frederick) Haddon, RA	1854	1924
		Sir William Crookes	1832	1919
1914	1933	Kenneth Alfred Wolfe Barry	1879	1936
	1934	Charles Langbridge Morgan	1855	1940
1919	1935	William Vaux Graham	1859	1940
		Sir William (Henry) Ellis	1860	1945
		Sir Glynn (Hamilton) West	1877	1945

Member	President		Born	Died
1919	1936	Ernest Frederic Crosbie Trench	1869	1960
	1937	Charles Pratt Sparks	1866	1940
	1938	John McFarlane Kennedy	1879	1954
		Donald Alexander Matheson	1860	1935
	1939	Thomas Garmondsway Wrightson	1871	1950
		Frederick Palmer	1862	1934
		Captain Matthew Henry Phineas Riall Sankey, RE	1853	1925
		William Henry Maw	1838	1924
		Harry Edward Jones	1843	1925
		Professor John Cunningham McLennan	1867	1935
1920		Sir John Purser Griffith	1848	1938
		Kenneth Phipson Hawksley	1869	1924
		Joseph Shaw, KC	1856	1933
		Sir Aston Webb, PRA	1849	1930
1921	1942	Sir Eustace (Henry) Tennyson-D'Eyncourt, Bart	1868	1951
		Sir John (Francis Cleverton) Snell	1869	1938
		William Archer Porter Tait	1866	1929
		Lieut. Col. James Forest Carmichael, RE	1868	1934
1922		William Wylie Grierson	1863	1935
		The Duke of Northumberland	1880	1930
		Sir (Harry Edwin) Bruce Bruce-Porter, MD	1869	1948
1923		*Rt Hon. Lord Ashfield*	1874	1948
		Sir Richard Threlfall	1861	1932
		Sir George (Thomas) Beilby	1850	1924
1924	1941	Sir Westcott (Stile) Abell	1877	1961
		Sir Henry (Percy) Maybury	1864	1943
		Sir Archibald (John Campbell) Ross	1867	1931
	1943	Maurice Fitzgerald Wilson	1858	1945
1925		David Hay	1859	1938
		George William Humphreys	1863	1945
		Sir James (Lyne) Devonshire	1863	1946
		Rear Admiral Sir Douglas Brownrigg, Bart	1867	1939
		Rt Hon. Hugh Pattison Macmillan, KC	1873	1952
1926		Enginer Vice Admiral Sir Robert (Bland) Dixon	1867	1939
		Sir Brodie (Haldane) Henderson	1869	1936
	1944	Sir John (Edward) Thornycroft	1872	1960
		Robert Reginald Johnston Turner	1879	1955

Member	President		Born	Died
1927	1945	Sir Richard (Augustine Studdart) Redmayne	1865	1955
	1946	William James Eames Binnie	1867	1949
		Sir Herbert (Ashcombe) Walker	1868	1949
1928		Edward Wyndham Monkhouse	1865	1940
1929		Sir William (John) Berry	1865	1937
		Sir Clement (Daniel Maggs) Hindley	1874	1944
	1947	Sir Alexander Gibb	1872	1958
		Seagar Berry	–	1932
		Sir William (Henry) Bragg	1862	1942
1930		Hugh Henry Gordon Mitchell	1874	1938
1931	1948	Sir Leopold (Halliday) Savile	1870	1953
	1949	Sydney Bryan Donkin	1871	1952
	1950	Sir Cyril (Reginald Sutton) Kirkpatrick	1872	1957
		Sir Lynden (Livingstone) Macassey, KC	1876	1963
1931		Robert Henry Thorpe	1860	1937
		Charles George Du Cane	1879	1941
1932	1951	Engineer Vice Admiral Sir Reginald (William) Skelton	1872	1956
		Sir Arthur (Henry) Preece	1867	1951
		Herbert Nigel Gresley	1876	1941
		Charles Ernest Christopher Browne	1871	1953
	1952	Sir Murdoch MacDonald, MP	1866	1957
		Sir Richard (Arman) Gregory, Bart	1864	1952
		Henry Archibald Sanders	–	1933
1933		*Col. Edward Geoffrey Hippisley Cox*	1884	1954
1934	1953	David Anderson	1880	1953
		Rustat Blake	1871	1940
1935	1954	William Thomson Halcrow	1883	1958
		Gerald William Partridge	1866	1940
1936		Engineer Vice Admiral Sir Harold (Arthur) Brown	1878	1968
		Sir Arthur (William) Johns	1873	1937
		William Everard Tyldesley Jones, KC	1874	1938
1937		Arthur Trevenen Coode	1876	1940
		Thomas Peirson Frank	1881	1951
		Harold John Frederick Gourley	1886	1956
		Colonel David Lyell	1866	1940
	1956	*Marmaduke Tudsbery Tudsbery	1892	1983
		Athol Lancelot Anderson	1875	1955
		Raymond Carpmael	1875	1950

Member	President		Born	Died
1937	1955	Lieutenant Colonel Jonathan Roberts Davidson	1874	1961
		Frederick Charles Cook	1875	1947
1938		John Duncan Watson	1860	1946
		Hon. Mr Justice George Langton, KC	1881	1942
1939		Dr Reginald Ewart Stradling	1891	1952
		Francis Ernest Wentworth-Shields	1869	1959
		Commander Sir Charles (Worthington) Craven, Bart	1884	1944
		Sir Maurice (Edward) Denny, Bart	1886	1955
1941		Roger Gaskill Hetherington	1876	1952
		Sir (Standen) Leonard Pearce	1873	1947
		Sir Harold (Edgar) Yarrow, Bart	1884	1962
		Alec George Vaughan-Lee	1868	1960
	1958	Thomas Edwin Hawksley	1897	1972
	1957	Vernon Alec Murray Robertson	1890	1971
		Edmund Graham Clark	1889	1954
1942		Professor Charles Edward Inglis	1875	1952
		Thomas Shirley Hawkins	1873	1952
	1959	Allan Stephen Quartermaine	1888	1978
		Lieut. Col. Sir John (Henry Maitland) Greenly	1885	1950
	1960	Major William Henry Morgan	1883	1966
	1961	Brigadier Bruce Gordon White	1885	1983
		Admiral of the Fleet, the Lord Chatfield	1873	1967
1943	1962	William Kelly Wallace	1883	1969
		Sir Stanley (Vernon) Goodall	1883	1965
		Colonel Charles Matthew Norrie	1883	1965
		John Duncan Campbell Couper	1876	1962
1945		Malcolm Gordon John McHaffie	1881	1958
	1963	Reginald Duncan Gwyther	1887	1965
		Sir Cecil (Thomas) Carr, KC	1878	1966
		Sir Henry (Thomas) Tizard	1885	1959
1946		William Lowe Lowe-Brown	1876	1956
1947	1964	John Garmondsway Wrighton	1911	1983
	1965	John Sunderland Langdale Train	1888	1969
	1966	George Matthew McNaughton	1893	1966
1948		Sir Stanley Angwin	1883	1959
		Sir Claude (Cavendish) Inglis	1883	1974
1949		Oliver Vaughan Snell Bulleid	1882	1970
		Rt Hon. Lord Brabazon of Tara	1910	1974
		Very Rev. Alan Campbell Don	1885	1966
		Sir William (Allen) Daley, MD	1887	1969

Member	President		Born	Died
1949	1967	Vice Admiral (E) Sir Denys (Chester) Ford	1890	1967
1950	1968	David Mowat Watson	1891	1972
		Arthur Clifford Hartley	1889	1960
		Sir Cyril (William) Hurcomb	1883	1975
		Kenneth S. Carpmael, KC	1885	1975
		Eustace Gervais Tennyson D'Eyncourt	1902	1971
		Sir William (Arthur) Stanier	1876	1965
		Edward Johnson Rimmer	1883	1962
1951		Sir Noel Ashbridge	1889	1975
		Richard William Foxlee	1885	1961
		Sir Charles (Swift) Lillicrap	1887	1966
		Maj. Gen. Gilbert Savil Szlumper	1884	1969
1952	1969	William Henry Glanville	1900	1976
		Sir (Alexander) Rowland Smith	1888	1988
1953	1971	*HRH the Prince Philip Duke of Edinburgh, KG, PC, KT*	1921	
		Sir (Frederick) Arthur Whitaker	1893	1968
	1970	*Geoffrey Morse Binnie	1908	1989
		Joseph Rawlinson	1897	1971
		Henry Francis Cronin	1894	1977
	1972	Reginald William Mountain	1899	1981
		Sir Walter (James) Drummond	1891	1965
1954		Professor Alfred John Sutton Pippard	1891	1969
		Maj. Gen. Charles Anderson Lane Dunphie	1902	
		Edward Humphrey Browne	1911	1987
1956	1973	*Harold John Boyer Harding	1900	1986
		Admiral the Earl Mountbatten of of Burma, KG, PC	1900	1979
		Rt Hon. the Viscount Falmouth	1887	1962
		Alexander McDonald	1903	1968
1957	1974	*John Elliot George Palmer	1904	1984
		Horace Denton Morgan	1904	1971
	1975	Reginald White Hawkey	1908	1978
		Sir Claude (Dixon) Gibb	1898	1959
	1976	*Sir Victor Shepheard	1893	
	1977	*Vice Admiral Sir Frank (Trowbridge) Mason	1900	1988
		Robert Meredydd Wynne-Edwards	1897	1974
1958		Sir Christopher Hinton	1901	1983
		George Ambler Wilson	1906	1977
		Sir Harold Bishop	1900	1983
1959		Sir George Nelson, Bart	1917	1962

Member	President		Born	Died
1959		Jack Duvivier	1901	1981
		Robin Riddles	1892	1983
		Marcus George Russell Smith	1901	
1960		*Sir Henry Jones	1906	1987
	1978	*Ralph Freeman	1911	
		*Roger Le Geyt Hetherington	1908	
		Sir James (Allan) Milne	1896	1966
	1979	*Cecil Robert Costeker Turner*	1910	
1961		Charles Malcolm Vignoles	1901	1961
	1980	*Thomas Angus Lyall Paton	1905	
		Admiral Sir Michael (Maynard) Denny	1896	1972
1962		Godfrey Thomas Verrall	1899	
		Charles Brand	1895	1966
		Frank Leslie Gordon	1886	1974
1963	1981	*Professor Alec Westley Skempton	1914	
	1982	*Douglas Cecil Coode	1908	
		Sir (Herbert) James Gunn	1893	1964
1966		John Holmes Jellett	1905	1971
		*Rudolph Glossop	1902	
	1983	Sir Eric (Grant) Yarrow, Bart	1920	
		Rear Admiral Peter Douglas Herbert Raymond Pelly	1904	1980
	1984	William Gordon Harris	1912	
		Sir Gilbert Roberts	1899	1978
	1985	Alfred Henry Cantrell	1903	
1967		Sir Eric Mensforth	1906	
		Peter Wilfred Essex Holloway	1908	
		Edward Irvine Halliday	1902	
		Sidney Alexander Finnis	1908	1969
	1986	John Walter Baxter	1917	
		Roland Curling Bond	1903	1980
		Oleg Alexander Kerensky	1905	1984
1968		Kingsley Charles Dunham	1910	
		Sir Alfred Sims	1907	1977
	1987	Rear Admiral John Garth Watson	1914	
1969		Sir Hubert Shirley-Smith	1901	1981
	1988	Sir (William) Kirby Laing	1916	
		His Honour Judge Mervyn Griffith-Jones, QC	1909	1979
1970		*Vice Admiral Sir (Robert) George Raper	1915	
		Archibald Paterson	1913	1981
		Major James Rennie Maudslay	1915	1988
1970		*Rt Hon. the Viscount Simon*	1902	

Member	President		Born	Died
		Hon. Sir Patrick, Mr Justice Graham, QC	1906	
1971	1989	Alan James Harris	1916	
		Sir (Robert) Edwin McAlpine	1907	
		Maj. Gen. Richard Lewis Clutterbuck	1917	
1972		*Angus Anderson Fulton	1900	1983
		Arthur David Holland	1913	
		Rt Rev. and Rt Hon. Dr Robert Wright Stopford, Lord Bishop of London	1901	1976
		Rt Hon. The Lord Mais	1911	
		David McKenna	1911	
1973		Professor Sir Alfred (Grenvile) Pugsley	1903	
		Maj. Gen. Michael Whitworth Prynne	1912	1977
1975		Alan Marshall Muir Wood	1921	
		Francis David Penney	1918	
		*Sir Norman (Andrew Forster) Rowntree	1912	
1976		Ian MacDonald Campbell	1922	
		Sir Derman (Guy) Christopherson	1915	
		John Vernon Bartlett	1927	
		John Anthony Derrington	1921	
		Nahum Noel Beryl Ordman	1919	
		Rear Admiral Douglas Grainger Parker	1919	
1977		Professor Reginald Charles Coates	1920	
		John Thornton Calvert	1907	1988
		Raymond Brian Hill	1921	1979
		James Gordon Wiltshire	1928	
		Rt Rev. Dr David Say, Lord Bishop of Rochester	1914	
1978		*Dennis Archibald Barrett*	1920	
		Sir (Harold) Montague Finniston	1912	
		Surgeon Vice Admiral Sir James Watt	1914	
1979		John McCallum	1920	
		Sir (Amos) Henry Chilver	1926	
		Sir Ove (Nyquist) Arup	1895	1988
		Vice Admiral Sir Philip (Alexander) Watson	1919	
1980		William George Nicholson Geddes	1913	
		Peter Arthur Cox	1922	

Member	President		Born	Died
1980		Maxwell Charles Purbrick	1926	
1981		Professor Sir Hugh Ford	1913	
		James Richard Samuel Morris	1925	
		James Anthony Gaffney	1928	
		Maj. Gen. Peter John Mitchell Pellereau	1921	
1982		Diarmuid Downs	1922	
		Thomas Leslie Grant Deuce	1932	
		Professor Jacques Heyman	1925	
		Dr Denis Rebbeck	1914	
1984		John Cormack McKenzie	1927	
		Charles Dargie Brown	1927	
		Kenneth Farish Scott	1918	
		Derek Barton Kimber	1917	
1985		Rt Hon. the Viscount Caldecote	1917	
		Air Marshal Sir Charles (Norman Seton) Pringle	1919	
		Maj. Gen. George Brian Sinclair	1928	
		Hon. William McAlpine	1937	
		David John Lee	1930	
1986		Sir Francis (Leonard) Tombs	1924	
		Sir Alec (Alexander Walter) Merrison	1924	
		J. Martin K. Laing	1942	
1987		David Gwilym Morris Roberts	1925	
		Thomas John Parker	1942	
1988		Ronald Jarman Bridle	1931	
		Donald Arthur David Reeve	1923	
		Sir Frank Gibb	1927	
		Alistair Craig Paterson	1924	
		John Charles Spencer Mott	1927	

Index